AWESOME
BIBLE
ACTIVITIES

COLLECTIONS 3 AND 4

Written by Vickie Save
Illustrated by Ken Save

BARBOUR
PUBLISHING, INC.
Uhrichsville, Ohio

© MCMXCVIII by Barbour Publishing, Inc.

ISBN 1-57748-356-1

All Scripture quotations, unless otherwise noted, are taken from the HOLY BIBLE,
NEW INTERNATIONAL VERSION®. NIV®. ©1973, 1978, 1984 by International Bible
Society. Used by permission of Zondervan Publishing House. All rights reserved.

Published by Barbour Publishing, Inc., P.O. Box 719, Uhrichsville, Ohio 44683
http://www.barbourbooks.com

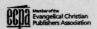
Member of the
Evangelical Christian
Publishers Association

Printed in the United States of America.

COLOR THE PICTURE

GOD IS THE CREATOR

FINISH THE VERSES

FINISH THE VERSES BY MATCHING THEM WITH THE PHRASES ON THE FOLLOWING PAGE.

1. "IN THE BEGINNING GOD CREATED...

_____

GENESIS 1:1

2. "AND GOD SAID, 'LET THERE BE LIGHT...'

_____

GENESIS 1:3

3. "AND GOD SAID, ' LET THERE BE AN EXPANSE BETWEEN...

_____

GENESIS 1:6

4. "SO GOD MADE AN EXPANSE AND SEPARATED...

_____

GENESIS 1:7

5. "AND IT WAS SO. GOD CALLED THE...

_____

GENESIS 1:8

6. "AND GOD SAID. 'LET THE WATER UNDER THE SKY...

_____

GENESIS 1:9

ANSWERS FOR THE PREVIOUS PAGE.

–THE HEAVENS AND THE EARTH."

–AND THERE WAS LIGHT."

– THE WATERS TO SEPARATE WATER FROM
WATER.'"

–THE WATER UNDER THE EXPANSE FROM THE
WATER ABOVE IT."

–EXPANSE 'SKY'."

–BE GATHERED TO ONE PLACE AND LET DRY
GROUND APPEAR.'"

CLICK!

FINISH THE VERSE

TO FIND OUT WHAT THE VERSE BELOW SAYS, FILL IN THE BLANKS. ALL THE CONSONANTS ARE THERE, SO ALL YOU NEED TO DO IS ADD THE VOWELS.

VOWELS: A E I O U

"G __ D C __ LL __ D TH __ DRY

GR __ __ ND 'L __ ND' __ ND TH __

G __ TH __ R __ D W __ T __ RS H __

C __ LL __ D 'S __ __ S'. __ ND G __ D

S __ W TH __ T __ T W __ S

G __ __ D."

GENESIS 1:10

4

FILL IN THE BLANKS

WORD LIST:

VEGETATION	SEED
LAND	TREES
THEIR	KINDS
PLANTS	FRUIT

"THEN GOD SAID, ' LET THE __ __ __ __

PRODUCE __ __ __ __ __ __ __ __ __ __:

SEED-BEARING __ __ __ __ __ __ AND

__ __ __ __ __ ON THE LAND THAT BEAR

__ __ __ __ __ WITH __ __ __ __ IN IT,

ACCORDING TO __ __ __ __ __ VARIOUS

KINDS.' "

GENESIS 1:11

TWICE THE FUN

UNSCRAMBLE THE UNDERLINED WORD IN EACH VERSE. THEN, ON THE OPPOSITE PAGE, FIND AND CIRCLE IT IN THE WORD SEARCH PUZZLE.

1. "AND GOD SAID, ' LET THERE BE <u>ILHGTS</u> IN THE EXPANSE OF THE SKY TO SEPARATE THE <u>AYD</u> FROM <u>HTGIN.</u>'

   GENESIS 1:14

2. "<u>OGD</u> MADE TWO GREAT LIGHTS—THE GREATER LIGHT TO GOVERN THE DAY AND THE LESSER LIGHT TO GOVERN THE NIGHT. HE ALSO MADE THE <u>SSRAT</u>."

   GENESIS 1:16

3. "SO GOD CREATED THE GREAT CREATURES OF THE <u>ESA</u> AND EVERY <u>GLINVI</u> AND <u>GMNOVI</u> THING WITH WHICH THE WATER TEAMS, ACCORDING TO THEIR KINDS, AND EVERY WINGED <u>DBRI</u> ACCORDING TO ITS <u>DKNI</u>."

   GENESIS 1:21

6

```
L  M  I  N     I  G     H     T
I  Y  K  E  S  F  K     Z
G  B  M  O  V  I  N     G
H  A  S  N  N  G  C     U
T  R  E  D  P  D  A     Y
S  T  A  R  S  O  U     O
L  I  V  I  N  G  I     O
F  E  Y  B  J  K  S     W
```

HI!

7

ZANY CODE BUSTER

USE THE CODE CHART BELOW TO DECODE THE MYSTERY VERSE.

CONT'D ON THE NEXT PAGE...

GENESIS 1:24

9

ZANY CODE BUSTER

TO DECODE THIS MYSTERY VERSE, LOOK AT EACH LETTER AND WRITE THE ONE THAT COMES <u>BEFORE</u> IT IN THE ALPHABET.

A B C D E F G H I J K L M N O P Q R
S T U V W X Y X

" __ __ __ __   __ __ __
   U I F O   H P E

__ __ __ __ ,   __ __ __
T B J E   M F U

__ __   __ __ __ __
V T   N B L F

__ __ __   __ __
N B O   J O

__ __ __   __ __ __
P V S   P X O

__ __ __ __ __ ,   __ __
J N B H F   J O

CONT'D ON THE NEXT PAGE...

$\overline{\text{P}}$ $\overline{\text{V}}$ $\overline{\text{S}}$ $\overline{\text{M}}$ $\overline{\text{J}}$ $\overline{\text{L}}$ $\overline{\text{F}}$ -

$\overline{\text{O}}$ $\overline{\text{F}}$ $\overline{\text{T}}$ $\overline{\text{T}}$."

GENESIS 1:26

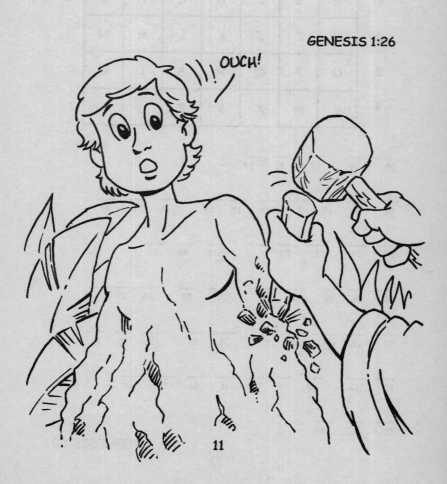

OUCH!

11

CODE BUSTER

USE THE CODE CHART BELOW TO COMPLETE THE VERSE. CHOOSE FROM THE LEFT SET OF NUMBERS FIRST. (Eg: 23=J)

	1	2	3	4	5	6	7
1	A	B	C	D	E	F	G
2	H	I	J	K	L	M	N
3	O	P	Q	R	S	T	U
4	V	W	X	Y	Z		

"
S O G O D
35 31 17 31 14

C R E A T E D M A N
13 34 15 11 36 15 14 26 11 27

I N H I S O W N
22 27 21 22 35 31 42 27

I M A G E ' I N T H E
22 26 11 17 15 22 27 36 21 15

I M A G E O F G O D
22 26 11 17 15 31 16 17 31 14

H E C R E A T E D
21 15 13 34 15 11 36 15 14

H I M ."
21 22 26

GENESIS 1:27

12

•DOT 2 DOT•

CONNECT THE DOTS

ADAM

13

UNSCRAMBLE THE VERSE

TO FIND OUT WHAT THE VERSE BELOW SAYS, FILL IN THE BLANKS. ALL THE VOWELS ARE THERE, SO ALL YOU NEED TO ADD ARE THE CONSONANTS.

B C D F G H J K L M N P Q R S T V W X Y Z

"NETH HET DLRO DGO DMEA A MWNAO MFOR HTE BIR EH DHA KTEAN TOU FO ANM."

"_ _ E _   _ _ E _ O _ _

_ O _   _ A _ E _ A

_ O _ A _   _ _ O _   _ _ E

_ I _   _ E _ A _

_ A _ E _ O U _ O _

_ A _ _."

GENESIS 2:22

14

FINISH THE PICTURE

THIS PICTURE LOOKS A LITTLE UNFINISHED,
DOESN'T IT? A LOT OF THINGS ARE LEFT OUT, SO
WHY DON'T YOU FINISH IT BY FILLING IN AS
MANY MISSING PIECES AS YOU CAN FIND.

15

LOOK-ALIKES

FIND AND CIRCLE SIX DIFFERENCES IN THE
TWO PICTURES BELOW.

AMAZING MAZES

AS YOU GO THROUGH THE MAZE, COLLECT THE
LETTERS AND COMPLETE THE STATEMENT BELOW.

GOD IS OUR _ _ _ _ _ _ _ _ .

SQUARE GAME

COLOR IN THE AREAS THAT HAVE A SQUARE TO
COMPLETE THE VERSE BELOW.

"GOD SAW ALL THAT HE HAD MADE, AND IT WAS
VERY __ __ __ __."

GENESIS 1:31

18

PICTURE FRAMES
WHAT COULD THE PICTURE BE?

DRAW EXACTLY WHAT IS IN EACH NUMBERED
FRAME AT THE TOP OF THE PAGE INTO EACH FRAME
OF THE SAME NUMBER IN THE GRID BELOW.

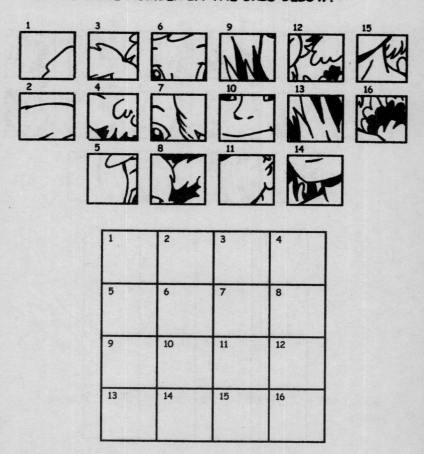

PICTURE FRAMES

WHAT COULD THE PICTURE BE?

DRAW EXACTLY WHAT IS IN EACH NUMBERED
FRAME AT THE TOP OF THE PAGE INTO EACH FRAME
OF THE SAME NUMBER IN THE GRID BELOW.

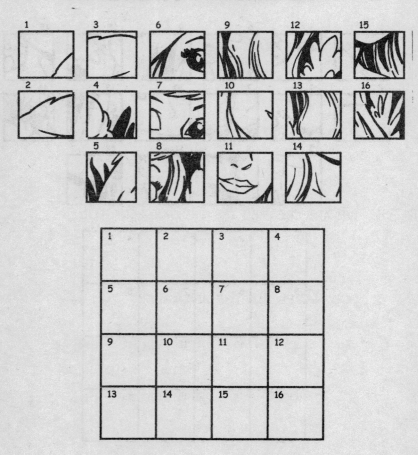

TRUE / FALSE

1. THE FIRST THING GOD CREATED WAS THE
   TREES.

                              TRUE ____ FALSE____

2. GOD SPOKE ALL CREATION INTO EXISTENCE.

                              TRUE ____ FALSE____

3. MAN CREATED WOMAN.

                              TRUE ____ FALSE____

4. WE ARE CREATED IN THE IMAGE OF GOD.

                              TRUE ____ FALSE____

5. GOD NAMED ALL THE ANIMALS.

                              TRUE ____ FALSE____

WORD SEARCH

CROSS OUT EVERY LETTER THAT APPEARS AT LEAST FOUR TIMES IN THE PUZZLE TO FIND THE WORD THAT COMPLETES THE SENTENCE.

```
B F S J N D L S
Q X C W A G X Q
V N L D J S C V
Q G X B S T V G
C J W V N Q B V
B L H G C E D J
W N D X R C L W
```

GOD THE _ _ _ _ _ _ .

UNSCRAMBLE THE VERSE

TO FIND OUT WHAT THE VERSE BELOW SAYS, FILL
IN THE BLANKS. ALL THE VOWELS ARE THERE, SO
ALL YOU NEED TO ADD ARE THE CONSONANTS.

B C D F G H J K L M N P Q R S T V W X Z

"A RHTFAE OT HTE HREFATSELS, A FRDDENEE FO
DWSOIW, SI DGO NI SIH YHLO WGNDILEL."

"A __A__ __E__ __O ___E

__A__ __E__ __E__ __, A

__E__E__ __E__ O__ __I__O__ __,

I__ __O__ I__ __I__ __O__Y

__ __E__ __I__ __."

PSALM 68:5

23

CODE BUSTER

USE THE CODE CHART BELOW TO COMPLETE THE VERSE. CHOOSE FROM THE LEFT SET OF NUMBERS FIRST. (Eg: 23=J)

	1	2	3	4	5	6	7
1	A	B	C	D	E	F	G
2	H	I	J	K	L	M	N
3	O	P	Q	R	S	T	U
4	V	W	X	Y	Z		

"
__ __   __ __ __ __   __ __ __ __   __ __ __
21 15   42 22 25 25   13 11 25 25   31 37 36

__ __   __ __ ,   __ __ __   __ __ __   __ __
36 31   26 15   44 31 37   11 34 15   26 44

__ __ __ __ __ __ ,   __ __   __ __ __ ,
16 11 36 21 15 34   26 44   17 31 14

__ __ __   __ __ __ __ ,   __ __
36 21 15   34 31 13 24   26 44

__ __ __ __ __ __ __ .''
35 11 41 22 31 37 34

PSALM 89:26

AMAZING MAZES

ADAM AND EVE ARE PLAYING HIDE AND SEEK. BUT THE GARDEN IS SO BIG, THAT ADAM IS HAVING A HARD TIME FINDING EVE. CAN YOU HELP HIM FIND THE WAY?

TWICE THE FUN

UNSCRAMBLE THE UNDERLINED WORDS IN THE VERSE. THEN, ON THE OPPOSITE PAGE, FIND AND CIRCLE THEM IN THE WORD SEARCH PUZZLE.

"BUT YOU ARE OUR <u>HFARET</u>, THOUGH ABRAHAM DOES NOT <u>ONWK</u> US OR <u>SLIEAR</u> ACKNOWLEDGE US; YOU O <u>RLDO</u>, ARE <u>URO</u> FATHER, OUR <u>DMEREERE</u>."

_ _ _ _ _ _   _ _ _ _

_ _ _ _ _ _   _ _ _ _

_ _   _   _ _ _ _ _ _ _

ISAIAH 63:16

CONT'D ON THE NEXT PAGE...

R G A N L S W K
E Y Q H J O U R
D L D V N F R Z
E W T K A A K D
E J C L Y T X U
M Q Z I B H O F
E I S R A E L E
R W D Y Z R P J

ZANY CODE BUSTER

TO DECODE THIS MYSTERY VERSE, LOOK AT EACH LETTER AND WRITE THE ONE THAT COMES <u>BEFORE</u> IT IN THE ALPHABET.

A B C D E F G H I J K L M N O P Q R
S T U V W X Y Z

" __ __   __ __ __   __ __ __ __   __ __ __ ,
  J O   U I F   T B N F   X B Z

__ __ __   __ __ __ __   __ __ __ __ __
M F U   Z P V S   M J H I U

__ __ __ __ __   __ __ __ __ __ __   __ __ __ '
T I J O F   C F G P S F   N F O

__ __ __ __   __ __ __ __   __ __ __
U I B U   U I F Z   N B Z

__ __ __   __ __ __ __   __ __ __ __
T F F   Z P V S   H P P E

__ __ __ __ __   __ __ __   __ __ __ __ __ __
E F F E T   B O E   Q S B J T F

CONT'D ON THE NEXT PAGE...

Z P V S   G B U I F S   J O

I F B W F O ."

MATTHEW 5:16

NO!
NOT *THAT*
KIND OF LIGHT!

COLOR THE COMIC

CONT'D ON THE NEXT PAGE...

30

ZANY CODE BUSTER

USE THE CODE CHART BELOW TO DECODE THE MYSTERY VERSE.

CONT'D ON THE NEXT PAGE...

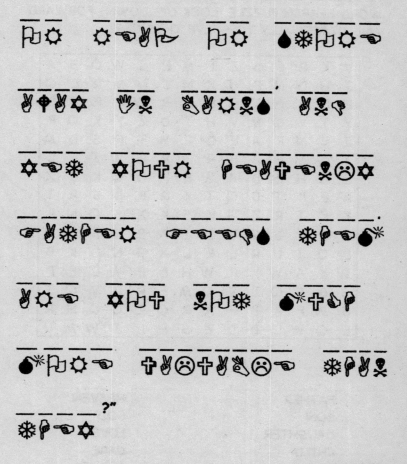

MATTHEW 6:26

WORD SEARCH

FIND AND CIRCLE THE WORDS BELOW IN THE
WORD SEARCH PUZZLE. LOOK UP, DOWN, FORWARD
AND DIAGONALLY TO SOLVE THIS ONE!

```
V K R G S Z I M E Q W O S A
J H D M E U X N C D M R L Q
H D F A T H E R B W G P G D
Y T Y Q M V H T D Z Y K O P
J K N P A E D E W T F S D M
T Q M E A F R J R H W T B L
E S H J D A W E H D Q K C X
R E P T C Q T K R P B C R T
K F T R Z H K S K X S Q N L
P G L I G Y I Z P B O F C N
L O J U R L P L X G N D K B
W K A W Y P W H D P W L E P
S D S Q I V Q M F R D V Q T
G W F P B F X R Q Z O C H R
L Q W L D D Z S H L J W M U
```

FATHER	HEAVEN
SON	GOD
DAUGHTER	LOVE
CHILD	CARE

34

FINISH THE VERSE

TO FIND OUT WHAT THE VERSE BELOW SAYS, FILL
IN THE BLANKS. ALL THE CONSONANTS ARE THERE,
SO ALL YOU NEED TO DO IS ADD THE VOWELS.

VOWELS: A E I O U

"_ W_LL B_ _ F_TH_R T_

Y_ _ _ND Y_ _ _ W_LL B_

MY S_NS _ND D_ _GHT_RS."

2 CORINTHIANS 6:18

35

UNSCRAMBLE AND ANSWER

FIRST, UNSCRAMBLE THE WORDS AND WRITE THEM IN THE SPACE BELOW. THEN, ON THE FOLLOWING PAGE, LIST ALL THE CIRCLED LETTERS AND UNSCRAMBLE THEM TO SPELL OUT THE ANSWER TO THE QUESTION.

"ON EON SHA ENSE HTE HTRAFE

___ ___ ◯___ ____ ___◯___

CTEPXE HET EON HWO SI RMFO

_____ ___ ___ ___ ___ __ ___◯

DGO; NYOL EH SHA ENSE HTE

___ ___ ___ ___◯___ ___◯___

EAHFRT."

___◯___

JOHN 6:46

CONT'D ON THE NEXT PAGE...

36

CONT'D FROM THE PREVIOUS PAGE.

◯ ◯ ◯ ◯ ◯ ◯
‾ ‾ ‾ ‾ ‾ ‾

GOD IS OUR HEAVENLY _ _ _ _ _ _ !

FINISH THE VERSE

TO FIND OUT WHAT THE VERSE BELOW SAYS, FILL
IN THE BLANKS. ALL THE CONSONANTS ARE THERE,
SO ALL YOU NEED TO DO IS ADD THE VOWELS.

VOWELS: A E I O U

"MY F_TH_R, WH_ H_S

G_V_N TH_M T_ M_ _S

GR_ _T_R TH_N _LL; N_

_N_ C_N SN_TCH TH_M

_ _T _F MY F_TH_R'S

H_ND. _ _ND TH_ F_TH_R

_R_ _N_."

JOHN 10:29-30

38

HIDDEN ALPHABET

FIND AND CIRCLE EVERY LETTER OF THE ALPHABET THAT HAS BEEN HIDDEN IN THIS PICTURE.

FINISH THE PICTURE

USING THE GRID, DRAW THE PICTURE BELOW ON
THE FOLLOWING PAGE.

IN THE FATHER'S HAND!

FROM THE PREVIOUS PAGE, USE THE GRID TO
DRAW THE PICTURE FOR YOURSELF.

41

CODE BUSTER

USE THE CODE CHART BELOW TO COMPLETE THE VERSE. CHOOSE FROM THE LEFT SET OF NUMBERS FIRST. (Eg: 23=J)

	1	2	3	4	5	6	7
1	A	B	C	D	E	F	G
2	H	I	J	K	L	M	N
3	O	P	Q	R	S	T	U
4	V	W	X	Y	Z		

" J   E   S   U   S   S   A   I   D ,   D   O
  23 15 35 37 35   35 11 22 14   14 31

 N   O   T   H   O   L   D   O   N   T   O
27 31 36   21 31 25 14   31 27   36 31

 M   E   F   O   R   I   H   A   V   E
26 15   16 31 34   22   21 11 41 15

 N   O   T   Y   E   T   R   E   T   U   R   N   E   D
27 31 36   44 15 36   34 15 36 37 34 27 15 14

 T   O   T   H   E   F   A   T   H   E   R .
36 31   36 21 15   16 11 36 21 15 34

CONT'D ON THE NEXT PAGE...

```
__  __    __  __  __  __  __  __  __     __  __    __  __
17  31    22  27  35  36  15  11  14     36  31    26  44

__  __  __  __  __  __  __  __     __  __  __
12  34  31  36  21  15  34  35     11  27  14

__  __  __  __    __  __  __  __ ,  "  __     __  __
36  15  25  25    36  21  15  26     22     11  26

__  __  __  __  __  __  __  __  __     __  __    __  __
34  15  36  37  34  27  22  27  17     36  31    26  44

__  __  __  __  __  __     __  __  __     __  __  __  __
16  11  36  21  15  34     11  27  14     44  31  37  34

__  __  __  __  __  __ ,   __  __    __  __    __  __  __
16  11  36  21  15  34     36  31    26  44    17  31  14

__  __  __    __  __  __  __    __  __  __ . " " "
11  27  14    44  31  37  34    17  31  14
```

JOHN 20:17

43

WORD SEARCH

HOW MANY TIMES CAN YOU FIND THE WORD
<u>FATHER</u> IN THE WORD SEARCH PUZZLE BELOW.
LOOK UP, DOWN, FORWARD AND DIAGONALLY TO
SOLVE THIS ONE!

```
R S K L Y B D T S F J F K Z
P F D J Z F G T X Y L A V T
X G A F S P R K D J B T Z S
K J L T D E Y F Z G V H X P
F T D X H P G J S L B E Z F
S Z V T F E L T D Y X R G J
B G A D B J R F Z F P B T V
L F Y X F Z G P V A L J D B
D Z S J L B K F Y T X S L K
T K P F D T F A T H E R X D
P L B Y J K Z D X E K B L F
F K F A T H E R Y R Y D T J
```

44

SQUARE GAME

COLOR IN THE AREAS THAT HAVE A SQUARE TO COMPLETE THE SENTENCE BELOW.

GOD IS <u>MY</u> __ __ __ __ __ __ !

COLOR THE PICTURE

GOD THE SON

FILL IN THE BLANKS

WORD LIST:

LOVE	AM
HIM	PLEASED
THIS	HEAVEN
VOICE	SON

"AND A _ _ _ _ _ FROM _ _ _ _ _ _

SAID, '_ _ _ _ IS MY _ _ _, WHOM I

_ _ _ _; WITH _ _ _ I _ _ WELL

_ _ _ _ _ _ _ .'"

MATTHEW 3:17

47

FINISH THE VERSE

TO FIND OUT WHAT THE VERSE BELOW SAYS, FILL IN THE BLANKS. ALL THE CONSONANTS ARE THERE SO ALL YOU NEED TO DO IS ADD THE VOWELS.

VOWELS: A E I O U

"__LL TH__NGS H__V__ B___N

C__MM__TT__D T__ M__ BY MY

F__TH__R. N__ __N__ KN__WS

TH__ S__N __XC__PT TH__

F__TH__R, __ND N__ __N__

KN__WS TH__ F__TH__R

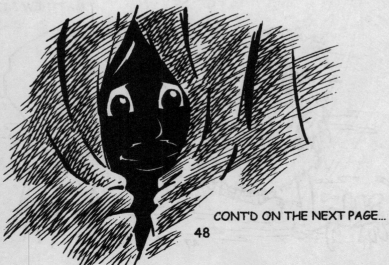

CONT'D ON THE NEXT PAGE...

48

__XC__PT TH__ S__N __ND
TH__S__ T__ WH__M TH__
S__N CH___S__S T__
R__V___L H__M."

MATTHEW 11:27

49

ZANY CODE BUSTER

TO DECODE THIS MYSTERY VERSE, LOOK AT EACH LETTER AND WRITE THE ONE THAT COMES <u>BEFORE</u> IT IN THE ALPHABET.

A B C D E F G H I J K L M N O P Q R
S T U V W X Y Z

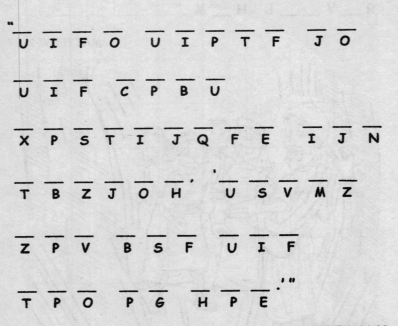

"T H E N — T H O S E — I N
U I F O — U I P T F — J O

T H E — B O A T
U I F — C P B U

W O R S H I P E D — H I M
X P S T I J Q F E — I J N

S A Y I N G, 'T R U L Y
T B Z J O H, ' U S V M Z

Y O U — A R E — T H E
Z P V — B S F — U I F

S O N — O F — G O D.'"
T P O — P G — H P E

MATTHEW 14:33

50

FINISH THE PICTURE

USING THE GRID, COMPLETE THE PICTURE BY
DUPLICATING THE FINISHED HALF ONTO THE
UNFINISHED AREA. TWO SQUARES HAVE ALREADY
BEEN STARTED FOR YOU.

JESUS, THE SON OF GOD

TWICE THE FUN

UNSCRAMBLE THE UNDERLINED WORDS IN EACH VERSE. THEN, ON THE OPPOSITE PAGE, FIND AND CIRCLE THEM IN THE WORD SEARCH PUZZLE.

1. "SIMON PETER ANSWERED, ' YOU ARE THE <u>RSITHC</u>, THE <u>NSO</u> OF THE LIVING <u>OGD</u>.'"

MATTHEW 16:16

_ _ _ _ _ _   _ _ _   _ _ _

2. "A <u>COVEI</u> CAME FROM THE <u>UCDOL</u>, SAYING, 'THIS IS MY SON WHOM I HAVE CHOSEN; <u>ETLINS</u> TO <u>IMH</u>.'"

LUKE 9:35

_ _ _ _ _   _ _ _ _ _

_ _ _ _ _ _   _ _ _

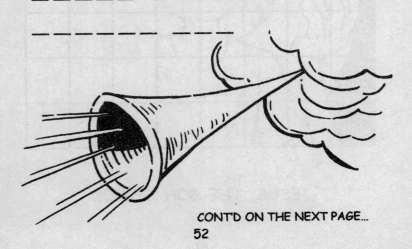

CONT'D ON THE NEXT PAGE...

CONT'D FROM THE PREVIOUS PAGE.

```
J  R  E  V  P  S  Z  Q  K
L  C  L  O  U  D  F  M  T
N  B  C  I  W  L  Q  B  W
H  N  J  C  H  R  I  S  T
H  Y  H  E  B  G  G  O  D
L  I  S  T  E  N  K  N  Z
M  J  M  W  D  Q  R  S  J
```

WORD JUMBLE

FILL IN THE BLANK SPACES BY WRITING IN THE
OPPOSITE OF EACH WORD BELOW, ANSWERING
EACH CLUE CORRECTLY. USING THE LETTERS IN THE
CIRCLES, COMPLETE THE SENTENCE BELOW.

MOTHER   — — — — — —

DAUGHTER   — ◯ —

DARK   — — — — —

END   — ◯ — — — — —

NIGHT   ◯ — —

MAN   — — — —

THE FATHER AND THE SON ARE BOTH :

◯ ◯ ◯

54

WORD SEARCH

HOW MANY TIMES CAN YOU FIND THE WORD, <u>SON</u>
BELOW IN THE WORD SEARCH PUZZLE? LOOK UP,
DOWN, FORWARD AND DIAGONALLY TO SOLVE
THIS ONE!

B	K	H	Z	P	T	F	S	C	J	R	Z	H	N
T	S	R	J	Z	X	N	W	B	M	K	P	O	Z
Z	F	O	C	H	S	P	R	Z	T	J	S	F	C
P	S	T	N	B	K	F	C	Q	H	X	Z	R	P
C	R	J	Z	P	S	X	T	M	S	B	F	E	K
S	T	H	F	K	R	C	Z	J	O	P	X	S	T
O	B	Z	P	S	T	X	Q	F	N	C	K	H	J
N	J	F	R	M	C	Z	S	P	J	X	F	T	Z
T	K	S	O	N	H	B	W	R	Z	M	C	P	S
C	J	P	R	T	N	S	N	K	F	J	S	R	B
Z	B	F	K	O	C	P	Z	T	S	C	O	H	X
P	H	T	S	C	R	F	B	S	J	K	N	B	Z

55

UNSCRAMBLE AND ANSWER

FIRST, UNSCRAMBLE THE WORDS AND WRITE THEM IN THE SPACES UNDER EACH WORD. THEN LIST ALL THE CIRCLED LETTERS BELOW AND UNSCRAMBLE THEM TO SPELL OUT THE ANSWER TO THE QUESTION.

"OFR   DGO   OS   VEOLD   ETH

_ _ _ _ ( ) _ ( ) _ _ _ _ _ _ _ _ _

LRWDO   AHTT   EH   EGVA   IHS

( ) _ _ _ _ _ _ _ _ _ _ _ _ _ _ _ _ _

NEO   DAN   LOYN   NSO."

( ) _ _ _ _ _ ( ) _ _ _ ( ) _ _

JOHN 3:16

WHO IS JESUS CHRIST?

( ) ( ) ( ) ( )' ( ) ( ) ( ) ( )!

56

AMAZING MAZES

AS YOU GO THROUGH THE MAZE, COLLECT THE
LETTERS AND COMPLETE THE STATEMENT BELOW.

GOD _ _ _ _ _ _ _ ME.

FINISH THE VERSE

TO FIND OUT WHAT THE VERSE BELOW SAYS, FILL IN THE BLANKS. ALL THE CONSONANTS ARE THERE, SO ALL YOU NEED TO DO IS ADD THE VOWELS.

VOWELS: A E I O U

"F _ TH _ R, TH _ T _ M _ H _ S

C _ ME. GL _ R _ FY Y _ _ R

S _ N, TH _ T Y _ _ R S _ N

M _ Y GL _ R _ FY Y _ _ _ ."

JOHN 17:1

58

WORD SEARCH

FIND AND CIRCLE THE WORDS BELOW IN THE
WORD SEARCH PUZZLE. LOOK UP, DOWN, FORWARD
AND DIAGONALLY TO SOLVE THIS ONE!

```
R D B K V T J S Z C F G L X
V J S C H R I S T D R B K T
T Z C X D B K F I V G J S C
F G K J R T V S M B Z X D L
S B J C Z X L J E F T K R É
D T E V K B S C Z G X S V J
J R S X C D O V K B F O Z T
B V U K T S N X J R L D G C
C Z S D J B C F T V S L K X
S G X K R T Z D L C J W B Q
V B D F A T H E R K T S Z R
J Z L T R K V B S J X D G C
G C X S Z D J T G C L V K B
O T K V B R G L O R I F Y D
D S C D X J Z K V T B R S J
```

CHRIST   TIME
GOD   GLORIFY
JESUS   SON
LOVE   FATHER

59

CODE BUSTER

USE THE CODE CHART BELOW TO COMPLETE THE VERSE. CHOOSE FROM THE LEFT SET OF NUMBERS FIRST. (Eg: 23=J)

	1	2	3	4	5	6	7
1	A	B	C	D	E	F	G
2	H	I	J	K	L	M	N
3	O	P	Q	R	S	T	U
4	V	W	X	Y	Z		

"
‾‾ ‾‾ ‾‾   ‾‾ ‾‾ ‾‾   ‾‾ ‾‾ ‾‾ ‾‾ ‾‾ ‾‾ ‾‾
11 27 14 42 21 31 36 21 34 31 37 17 21

‾‾ ‾‾ ‾‾   ‾‾ ‾‾ ‾‾ ‾‾ ‾‾ ‾‾   ‾‾ ‾‾
36 21 15 35 32 22 34 22 36 31 16

‾‾ ‾‾ ‾‾ ‾‾ ‾‾ ‾‾ ‾‾ ‾‾   ‾‾ ‾‾ ‾‾
21 31 25 22 27 15 35 35 42 11 35

‾‾ ‾‾ ‾‾ ‾‾ ‾‾ ‾‾ ‾‾ ‾‾   ‾‾ ‾‾ ‾‾ ‾‾
14 15 13 25 11 34 15 14 42 22 36 21

‾‾ ‾‾ ‾‾ ‾‾ ‾‾   ‾‾ ‾‾   ‾‾ ‾‾   ‾‾ ‾‾ ‾‾
32 31 42 15 34 36 31 12 15 36 21 15

‾‾ ‾‾ ‾‾   ‾‾ ‾‾   ‾‾ ‾‾ ‾‾
35 31 27 31 16 17 31 14

CONT'D ON THE NEXT PAGE...

___ ___ ___ ___ ___ ___ ___ ___ ___ ___ ___ ___ ___ -
12 44 21 22 35   34 15 35 37 34 34 15 13

___ ___ ___ ___ ___ ___ ___ ___ ___ ___ ___
36 22 31 27   16 34 31 26   36 21 15

___ ___ ___ ___ : ___ ___ ___ ___ ___ ___ ___ ___ ___ ___ ___
14 15 11 14   23 15 35 37 35   13 21 34 22 35 36

___ ___ ___ ___ ___ ___ ___ . "
31 37 34   25 31 34 14

ROMANS 1:4

ZANY CODE BUSTER

USE THE CODE CHART BELOW TO DECODE THE MYSTERY VERSE.

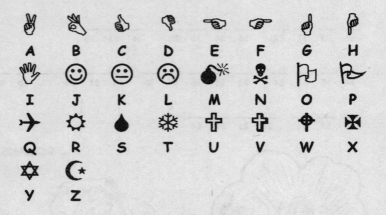

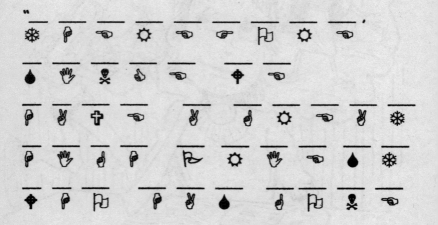

CONT'D ON THE NEXT PAGE...

CONT'D FROM THE PREVIOUS PAGE.

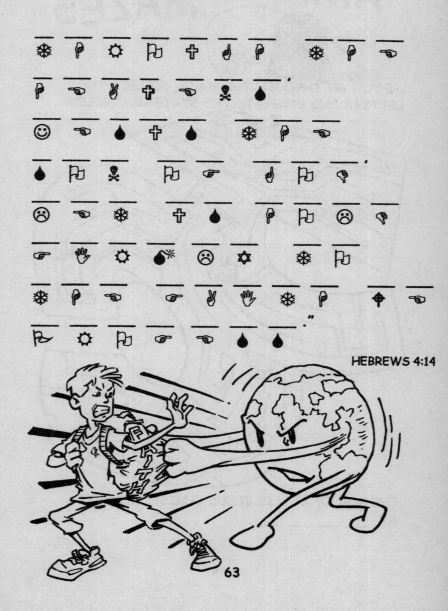

HEBREWS 4:14

AMAZING MAZES

AS YOU GO THROUGH THE MAZE, COLLECT THE
LETTERS AND COMPLETE THE STATEMENT BELOW.

THE SON OF GOD IS JESUS CHRIST...JESUS IS
MY __ __ __ __ .

ZANY CODE BUSTER

TO DECODE THIS MYSTERY VERSE, LOOK AT EACH LETTER AND WRITE THE ONE THAT COMES <u>BEFORE</u> IT IN THE ALPHABET.

A B C D E F G H I J K L M N O P Q R
S T U V W X Y Z

"_ _ _   _ _ _ _ _   _ _ _ _ _ _
 B O E   F W F S Z   U P O H V F

_ _ _ _ _ _ _   _ _ _ _
D P O G F T T   U I B U

_ _ _ _ _   _ _ _ _ _ _   _ _
K F T V T   D I S J T U   J T

_ _ _ _ _,   _ _   _ _ _
M P S E   U P   U I F

_ _ _ _ _   _ _   _ _ _   _ _ _
H M P S Z   P G   H P E   U I F

_ _ _ _ _ _."
G B U I F S

FINISH THE PICTURE

THIS PICTURE LOOKS A LITTLE UNFINISHED,
DOESN'T IT? A LOT OF THINGS ARE LEFT OUT, SO
WHY DON'T YOU FINISH IT BY FILLING IN AS
MANY MISSING PIECES AS YOU CAN FIND.

UNSCRAMBLE THE VERSE

TO FIND OUT WHAT THE VERSE BELOW SAYS, FILL IN THE BLANKS. ALL THE VOWELS ARE THERE, SO ALL YOU NEED TO ADD ARE THE CONSONANTS.

" OS EHNT, UTJS SA OYU ICEDVREE SEJUS TRHICS SA RLDO TUCNOINE OT ELVI NI IHM."

"_O __E_, _U__ A_ _OU

_E_EI_E_ _E_U_ ___I__

A_ _O__, _O__I_UE _O

_I_E I_ _I_."

COLOSSIANS 2:6

I THINK THERE'S MORE TO IT THAN THAT!

67

LOOK-ALIKES

FIND AND CIRCLE EIGHT DIFFERENCES IN THE
TWO PICTURES BELOW.

PICTURE FRAMES
WHAT COULD THE PICTURE BE?

DRAW EXACTLY WHAT IS IN EACH NUMBERED
FRAME AT THE TOP OF THE PAGE INTO EACH FRAME
OF THE SAME NUMBER IN THE GRID BELOW.

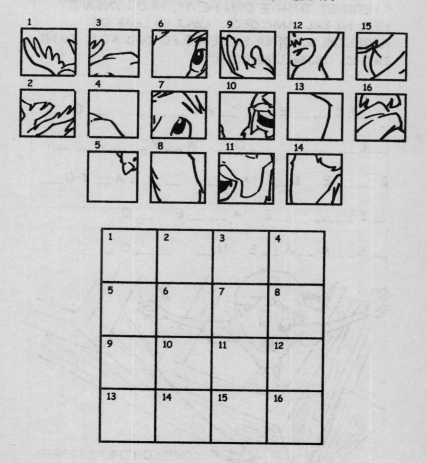

UNSCRAMBLE THE VERSE

TO FIND OUT WHAT THE VERSE BELOW SAYS, FILL IN THE BLANKS. ALL THE VOWELS ARE THERE, SO ALL YOU NEED TO ADD ARE THE CONSONANTS.

" HERINET IHGHTE ORN HEDTP, NRO HYNGANIT SELE NI LAL ANRTOECI, LWLI EB LEAB OT AARESTPE SU OFMR EHT EVLO FO OGD ATHT SI NI IRTHCS USJSE URO DOLR."

"__ E I __ __ E __   __ E I __ __ __   __ O __
__ E __ __ __ __ ,   __ O __   A __ Y __ __ I __ __
E __ __ E I __   A __ __   __ __ E A __ I O __
__ I __ __   __ E A __ __ E __ O
__ E __ A __ A __ E U __   __ __ O __

CONT'D ON THE NEXT PAGE...

__E _O_E O_ _O_

__A_ I_ I_ ___I__

_E_U_ OU_ _O__."

ROMANS 8:39

WORD SEARCH

CROSS OUT EVERY LETTER THAT APPEARS FOUR TIMES IN THE PUZZLE TO FIND THE WORD THAT COMPLETES THE SENTENCE.

```
H  V  B  J  S  G  Z  N
D  T  Z  X  P  C  B  T
T  P  S  F  I  K  F  K
G  J  N  Z  G  I  J  O
H  C  X  X  H  F  I  V
N  B  L  V  K  T  C  R
Z  G  I  P  J  S  N  B
S  X  K  C  F  V  P  H
```

JESUS IS ___ ___ ___ ___ OF ALL !

72

HIDDEN ALPHABET

FIND AND CIRCLE EVERY LETTER OF THE ALPHABET
THAT HAS BEEN HIDDEN IN THIS PICTURE.

73

CODE BUSTER

USE THE CODE CHART BELOW TO COMPLETE THE VERSE. CHOOSE FROM THE LEFT SET OF NUMBERS FIRST. (Eg: 23=J)

	1	2	3	4	5	6	7
1	A	B	C	D	E	F	G
2	H	I	J	K	L	M	N
3	O	P	Q	R	S	T	U
4	V	W	X	Y	Z		

"
A N D   W E   H A V E   S E E N
11 27 14 42 15 21 11 41 15 35 15 15 27

A N D   T E S T I F Y   T H A T
11 27 14 36 15 35 36 22 16 44 36 21 11 36

T H E   F A T H E R   H A S
36 21 15 16 11 36 21 15 34 21 11 35

S E N T   H I S   S O N   T O
35 15 27 36 21 22 35 35 31 27 36 31

B E   S A V I O U R   O F
12 15 35 11 41 22 31 37 34 31 16

T H E   W O R L D ."
36 21 15 42 31 34 25 14

1 JOHN 4:14

74

UNSCRAMBLE THE VERSE

TO FIND OUT WHAT THE VERSE BELOW SAYS, FILL
IN THE BLANKS. ALL THE VOWELS ARE THERE, SO ALL
YOU NEED TO ADD ARE THE CONSONANTS.

" OYU EAR LAL OSSN FO DGO GRUTHOH IFAHT NI
CSITRH SSEJU, OFR LAL FO UYO HOW EEWR
TBDEAPIZ TINO IRTHCS AEVH EDCOLHT
SSVEUERYOL HWTI RSICTH."

"__OU A__E A____ __O____ O__

__O__ _____OU____ __AI____

I__ _____I____ __E__U__, __O__

A____ O__ __OU ____O __E__E

__A____I__E__ I____O _____I____

__A__E ____O____E__ __OU__-

__E____E__ __I____ _____I____."

GALATIANS 3:26-27

COLOR THE COMIC

CONT'D ON THE NEXT PAGE...

HIDDEN ALPHABET

FIND AND CIRCLE EVERY LETTER OF THE ALPHABET THAT HAS BEEN HIDDEN IN THIS PICTURE. THEN, USING THOSE LETTERS, COMPLETE THE STATEMENT BELOW.

I AM GOD'S _ _ _ _ _ _ !

COLOR THE PICTURE

THE HOLY SPIRIT IS GOD

FINISH THE VERSE

TO FIND OUT WHAT THE VERSE BELOW SAYS, FILL IN THE BLANKS. ALL THE CONSONANTS ARE THERE, SO ALL YOU NEED TO DO IS ADD THE VOWELS.

VOWELS: A E I O U

"N __ W TH __   __ __ RTH W __ S

F __ RML __ SS __ ND __ MPTY

D __ RKN __ SS W __ S __ V __ R

TH __   S __ RF __ C __   __ F TH __

D __ __ P __ ND TH __   SP __ R __ T

__ F G __ D W __ S H __ V __ R __ NG

__ V __ R TH __   W __ T __ RS."

GENESIS 1:2

80

TWICE THE FUN

UNSCRAMBLE THE UNDERLINED WORDS IN EACH VERSE. THEN, ON THE NEXT PAGE, FIND AND CIRCLE THEM IN THE WORD SEARCH PUZZLE.

1. "WHERE CAN I GO FROM YOUR <u>TSIPIR</u>?"
   "WHERE CAN I FLEE FROM YOUR <u>EPRCENES</u>?"

   _ _ _ _ _ _   _ _ _ _ _ _ _ _

   PSALM 139:7

2. "I WILL <u>RPUO</u> OUT MY SPIRIT ON YOUR
   <u>GONFIFRSPR</u>."

   _ _ _ _   _ _ _ _ _ _ _ _ _

   ISAIAH 44:3

3. "AND I HAVE <u>DFEILL</u> HIM WITH THE SPIRIT OF
   <u>OGD</u>."

   _ _ _ _ _ _   _ _ _

   EXODUS 31:3

CONT'D ON THE NEXT PAGE...

D G P P F G H B O
S P I R I T V Y F
P L B E L U T Z F
O K D S L R N D S
U G H E E P V G P
R D K N D O G U R
H S Y C F O C R I
O S P E D K Y P N
D G H E Y C J J G

82

CODE BUSTER

USE THE CODE CHART BELOW TO COMPLETE THE VERSE. CHOOSE FROM THE LEFT SET OF NUMBERS FIRST. (Eg: 23=J)

	1	2	3	4	5	6	7
1	A	B	C	D	E	F	G
2	H	I	J	K	L	M	N
3	O	P	Q	R	S	T	U
4	V	W	X	Y	Z		

"
$\overline{22}$ $\overline{12}\,\overline{11}\,\overline{32}\,\overline{36}\,\overline{22}\,\overline{45}\,\overline{15}$ $\overline{44}\,\overline{31}\,\overline{37}$

$\overline{42}\,\overline{22}\,\overline{36}\,\overline{21}$ $\overline{42}\,\overline{11}\,\overline{36}\,\overline{15}\,\overline{34}$ $\overline{16}\,\overline{31}\,\overline{34}$

$\overline{34}\,\overline{15}\,\overline{32}\,\overline{15}\,\overline{27}\,\overline{36}\,\overline{11}\,\overline{27}\,\overline{13}\,\overline{15}$' $\overline{12}\,\overline{37}\,\overline{36}$

$\overline{11}\,\overline{16}\,\overline{36}\,\overline{15}\,\overline{34}$ $\overline{26}\,\overline{15}$ $\overline{42}\,\overline{22}\,\overline{25}\,\overline{25}$

$\overline{13}\,\overline{31}\,\overline{26}\,\overline{15}$ $\overline{31}\,\overline{27}\,\overline{15}$ $\overline{42}\,\overline{21}\,\overline{31}$ $\overline{22}\,\overline{35}$

CONT'D ON THE NEXT PAGE...

CONT'D FROM THE PREVIOUS PAGE.

___ ___ ___ ___   ___ ___ ___ ___ ___ ___ ___ ___
26 31 34 15   32 31 42 15 34 16 37 25

___ ___ ___ ___   ___ ,   ___ ___ ___ ___ ___
36 21 11 27   22   42 21 31 35 15

___ ___ ___ ___ ___ ___ ___   ___   ___ ___   ___ ___ ___
35 11 27 14 11 25 35   22   11 26   27 31 36

___ ___ ___   ___ ___   ___ ___ ___ ___ ___ .   ___ ___
16 22 36   36 31   13 11 34 34 44   21 15

___ ___ ___ ___   ___ ___ ___ ___ ___ ___ ___   ___ ___ ___
42 22 25 25   12 11 32 36 22 45 15   44 31 37

___ ___ ___ ___   ___ ___ ___   ___ ___ ___ ___
42 22 36 21   36 21 15   21 31 25 44

___ ___ ___ ___   ___ ___   ___ ___ ___   ___ ___ ___ ___ ."
35 32 22 34   22 36   11 27 14   16 22 34 15

WHOAA!

MATTHEW 3:11

UNSCRAMBLE THE VERSE

TO FIND OUT WHAT THE VERSE BELOW SAYS, FILL
IN THE BLANKS. ALL THE VOWELS ARE THERE, SO
ALL YOU NEED TO ADD ARE THE CONSONANTS.

"FI UYO NTEH, HTGHUO UYO EAR LEIV, WKON
WHO OT EGVI OOGD FGTSI OT RYUO NCHEIRDL,
WHO UMHC EMRO LWIL RYUO RTAHFE NI NHEEAV
EGVI HET YHOL TIIRPS OT ETSHO OWH KAS MHI!"

"I__ __OU __ __EN, __ __ OU__ __

__OU A__E E__I__, __ __ O__

__O__ __O __I__E __OO__

__I__ __ __ __O __OU__

__ __I__ __ __ __E__, __O__ __U__ __

__O__E __I__ __ __OU__

__A__ __E__ I__ __EA__E__

__I__E __ __E __O__ __ __ __I__I__

__O __ __O__E __ __O A__ __ __I__!"

LUKE 11:13

AMAZING MAZES

THE HOLY SPIRIT WANTS TO COME TO YOU. GO
THROUGH THE MAZE TO FIND THE PATH HE TAKES.

FILL IN THE BLANKS

WORD LIST:

COUNSELOR	REMIND
EVERYTHING	HOLY SPIRIT
NAME	FATHER
TEACH	THINGS

"BUT THE _ _ _ _ _ _ _ _ _ _ _ _ _, THE

_ _ _ _ _ _ _ _ _ _ _ _ _, WHOM THE

_ _ _ _ _ _ _ _ WILL SEND IN MY

_ _ _ _ _, WILL _ _ _ _ _ _ _ YOU ALL

_ _ _ _ _ _ _ _ AND WILL _ _ _ _ _ _ _ _

YOU OF _ _ _ _ _ _ _ _ _ _ _ _ _ _ _ I HAVE

SAID TO YOU."

JOHN 14:26

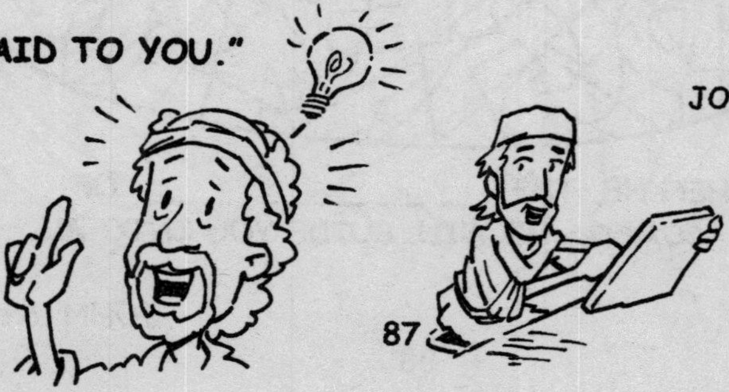

SQUARE GAME

COLOR IN THE AREAS THAT HAVE A SQUARE TO
FIND THE ANSWER TO COMPLETE THE VERSE BELOW.

"BUT WHEN HE, THE _ _ _ _ _ _ _ OF
TRUTH, COMES, HE WILL GUIDE YOU INTO ALL
TRUTH."

JOHN 16:13

LOOK-ALIKES

FIND AND CIRCLE TEN DIFFERENCES IN THE
TWO PICTURES BELOW.

ZANY CODE BUSTER

USE THE CODE CHART BELOW TO DECODE THE MYSTERY VERSE.

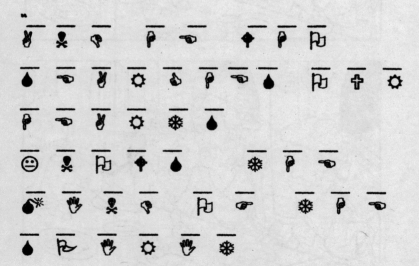

CONT'D ON THE NEXT PAGE...

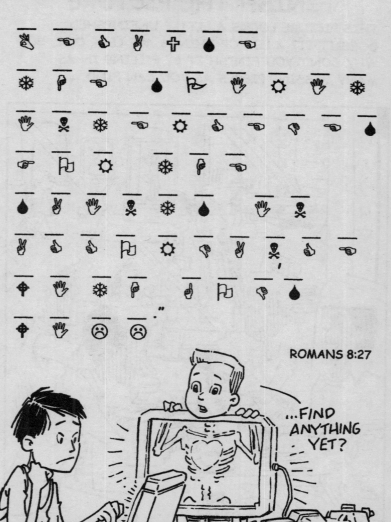

ROMANS 8:27

FINISH THE PICTURE

THIS PICTURE LOOKS A LITTLE UNFINISHED,
DOESN'T IT? A LOT OF THINGS ARE LEFT OUT, SO
WHY DON'T YOU FINISH IT BY FILLING IN AS
MANY MISSING PIECES AS YOU CAN FIND.

AMAZING MAZES

AS YOU GO THROUGH THE MAZE, COLLECT THE LETTERS AND COMPLETE THE VERSE BELOW.

"BUT GOD HAS REVEALED IT TO US BY HIS
__ __ __ __ __ __.   THE SPIRIT SEARCHES ALL
THINGS, EVEN THE DEEP THINGS OF GOD."

1 CORINTHIANS 2:10

CODE BUSTER

USE THE CODE CHART BELOW TO COMPLETE THE VERSE. CHOOSE FROM THE LEFT SET OF NUMBERS FIRST. (Eg: 23=J)

	1	2	3	4	5	6	7
1	A	B	C	D	E	F	G
2	H	I	J	K	L	M	N
3	O	P	Q	R	S	T	U
4	V	W	X	Y	Z		

"
W E   H A V E   N O T
42 15 21 11 41 15 27 31 36

R E C E I V E D   T H E
34 15 13 15 22 41 15 14 36 21 15

S P I R I T   O F   T H E
35 32 22 34 22 36 31 16 36 21 15

W O R L D ,   B U T   T H E
42 31 34 25 14   12 37 36 36 21 15

S P I R I T   W H O   I S
35 32 22 34 22 36 42 21 31 22 35

CON'T ON THE NEXT PAGE...

94

CONT'D FROM THE PREVIOUS PAGE.

—— —— —— ——   —— —— —— ,   —— —— —— ——   —— ——
16 34 31 26   17 31 14   36 21 11 36   42 15

—— —— ——   —— —— —— —— —— —— —— —— ——
26 11 44   37 27 14 15 34 35 36 11 27 14

—— —— —— ——   —— —— ——   —— —— ——
42 21 11 36   17 31 14   21 11 35

—— —— —— —— —— ——   —— —— —— —— ——
16 34 15 15 25 44   17 22 41 15 27

—— —— . "
37 35

GO AWAY!
I'VE TOLD YOU
BEFORE... I ALREADY
HAVE THE ONLY SPIRIT
I'LL EVER NEED!

1 CORINTHIANS 2:12

95

FILL IN THE BLANKS

"DO YOU NOT _ _ _ _ THAT _ _ _ _

_ _ _ _ IS A _ _ _ _ _ _ OF THE

_ _ _ _ _ _ _ _ _ _ _ WHO IS IN

_ _ _, WHOM YOU HAVE

_ _ _ _ _ _ _ _ _ FROM _ _ _?"

1 CORINTHIANS 6:19

DOES HE SEEM DIFFERENT TO YOU, TODAY?

UNSCRAMBLE AND ANSWER

FIRST, UNSCRAMBLE THE WORDS AND WRITE
THEM IN THE SPACES UNDER EACH WORD.THEN
LIST ALL THE CIRCLED LETTERS BELOW AND
UNSCRAMBLE THEM TO ANSWER THE QUESTION.

"EH   DAENTONI   SU,   TSE

◯___   _____   ___   ___

SHI   LSEA   FO   POIWHNSER

___   ___   ___   _____◯___

NO   SU   DAN   TPU   SHI   TPSIIR

___   ___   __◯___   ____   ____   _____

NI   RUO   SHTERA   SA   A

___   ___   _____   ___   __

CONT'D ON THE NEXT PAGE...

TDIESPO,   GGNUIAEREATN

_____ ___(O)_____

TWAH SI OT ECMO."

____ __ _ ___(O)_

2 CORINTHIANS 1:22

WHERE DOES THE HOLY SPIRIT LIVE?

IN MY (O)(O)(O)(O)(O) .

PICTURE FRAMES

WHAT COULD THE PICTURE BE?

DRAW EXACTLY WHAT IS IN EACH NUMBERED
FRAME AT THE TOP OF THE PAGE INTO EACH FRAME
OF THE SAME NUMBER IN THE GRID BELOW.

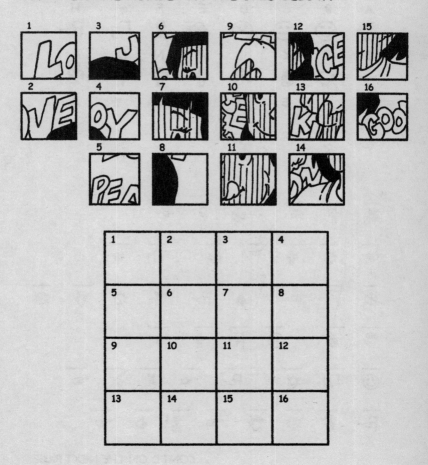

ZANY CODE BUSTER

USE THE CODE CHART BELOW TO DECODE THE MYSTERY VERSE.

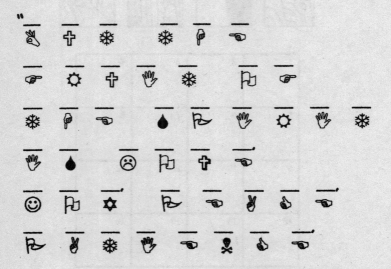

CONT'D ON THE NEXT PAGE...

GALATIANS 5:22

WORD SEARCH

HOW MANY TIMES CAN YOU FIND THE WORD
HOLY SPIRIT BELOW IN THE WORD SEARCH
PUZZLE. LOOK UP, DOWN, FORWARD, BACKWARDS
AND DIAGONALLY TO SOLVE THIS ONE!

```
H  D  S  F  G  J  L  C  K  V  P  Q  K  I
L  O  C  K  V  P  Q  K  I  D  J  G  F  S
H  O  L  Y  S  P  I  R  I  T  S  F  J  G
S  D  F  Y  G  J  K  I  Q  P  V  K  C  L
L  H  K  C  S  V  P  Q  S  K  J  G  D  F
H  O  L  Y  S  P  I  R  I  T  D  S  F  T
D  L  S  F  G  J  I  K  P  V  K  C  L  I
C  Y  L  K  V  K  P  R  S  D  J  G  F  R
S  S  H  O  L  Y  S  P  I  R  I  T  D  I
F  P  G  J  D  K  V  C  P  T  K  L  S  P
C  I  K  V  L  S  P  Q  K  G  F  D  J  S
D  R  F  G  J  C  Q  K  I  P  K  L  S  Y
S  I  P  G  K  K  L  D  V  C  J  G  F  L
F  T  I  R  I  P  S  Y  L  O  H  S  D  O
P  X  D  S  T  I  R  I  P  S  Y  L  O  H
```

102

COLOR THE COMIC

CONT'D ON THE NEXT PAGE...

CONT'D ON THE NEXT PAGE...

DOT 2 DOT

CONNECT THE DOTS

HIDDEN ALPHABET

FIND AND CIRCLE EVERY LETTER OF THE ALPHABET
THAT HAS BEEN HIDDEN IN THIS PICTURE AND
FINISH THE SENTENCE BELOW.

THE HOLY SPIRIT IS MY _ _ _ _ _ _ _.

MULTIPLE CHOICE

CIRCLE THE CORRECT ANSWER.

1. "IN THE BEGINNING GOD CREATED THE...

      A. SEA"
      B. HEAVENS AND EARTH"
      C. APPLE TREE"

2. GOD MADE MAN IN THE IMAGE OF...

      A. MONKEYS
      B MAN
      C. GOD

3. GOD CREATED EVE OUT OF ADAM'S...

      A. RIB
      B. ARM
      C. TOE

CONT'D ON THE NEXT PAGE...

CONT'D FROM THE PREVIOUS PAGE.

4. WE ARE CHILDREN OF...

        A. GOD
        B. ADAM
        C. OUR PARENTS

5. WHEN JESUS CALLED GOD, "ABBA", HE WAS SAYING...

        A. FATHER
        B. CREATOR
        C. LORD

6. WE BELIEVE IN...

        A. ONE GOD
        B. THREE GODS
        C. ONE GOD IN THREE PERSONS

TRUE / FALSE

1. A VOICE CAME FROM HEAVEN AND SAID "THIS IS JESUS."

   TRUE _____ FALSE_____

2. GOD CREATED EVE.

   TRUE _____ FALSE_____

3. JESUS CHRIST IS THE SON OF GOD.

   TRUE _____ FALSE_____

4. JESUS USED HIS GODLY POWERS DURING HIS MINISTRY.

   TRUE _____ FALSE_____

5. JESUS IS SAVIOUR OF THE WORLD.

   TRUE _____ FALSE_____

TRUE / FALSE

1. WE BECOME CHILDREN OF GOD BY GOING TO CHURCH.

   TRUE ____ FALSE____

2. THE HOLY SPIRIT WAS WITH GOD WHEN HE CREATED THE HEAVENS AND THE EARTH.

   TRUE ____ FALSE____

3. GOD THE FATHER WILL GIVE YOU THE HOLY SPIRIT, IF YOU ASK.

   TRUE ____ FALSE____

4. THE HOLY SPIRIT DOESN'T KNOW MY MIND AND HEART.

   TRUE ____ FALSE____

5. THE HOLY SPIRIT IS GOD.

   TRUE ____ FALSE____

COLOR THE PICTURE

WHAT IS GOD'S CHARACTER?
WHAT IS HE LIKE?
CONTINUE ON TO FIND OUT!

TWICE THE FUN

UNSCRAMBLE THE UNDERLINED WORDS IN THE VERSE BELOW. THEN, ON THE NEXT PAGE, FIND AND CIRCLE THEM IN THE WORD SEARCH PUZZLE.

"YOURS, O LORD, IS THE GREATNESS AND THE RPEOW AND THE YGRLO AND THE MAJESTY AND THE SPLENDOR, FOR EVERYTHING IN NHEEAV AND HETAR IS SYRUO. YOURS, O LORD, IS THE KMDOIDNG; YOU ARE EXALTED AS DHAE OVER ALL. WEALTH AND HONOR COME FROM UYO; YOU ARE THE REURL OF ALL STGHNI. IN YOUR HANDS ARE STRENGTH AND POWER TO EXALT AND EGVI STRENGTH TO ALL."

— — — — —   — — — — —

— — — — — —   — — — — —

— — — — —   — — — — — —

— — — —   — — —   — — — — —

— — — — — —   — — — —

1 CHRONICLES 29:11-12

GOD IS KING OF THE UNIVERSE.

CONT'D ON THE NEXT PAGE...

```
K  S  V  B  T  R  U  L  E  R
Y  I  Q  T  K  J  B  V  S  T
G  B  N  V  S  Y  Q  Y  Y  H
S  I  T  G  L  O  R  Y  O  I
T  B  V  Y  D  U  P  V  U  N
V  Q  S  E  B  O  K  Y  R  G
H  B  T  Q  W  S  M  Y  S  S
E  S  H  E  A  V  E  N  B  V
A  B  R  V  Q  K  Y  J  S  T
D  V  T  B  S  E  A  R  T  H
```

AMAZING MAZES

SOMETIMES, LIFE CAN SEEM LIKE A MAZE AND IT
IS HARD TO FIND THE WAY. IT IS GOOD TO KNOW
THAT WE ARE ALWAYS IN GOD'S HAND AND HE
KNOWS THE WAY WE SHOULD GO.

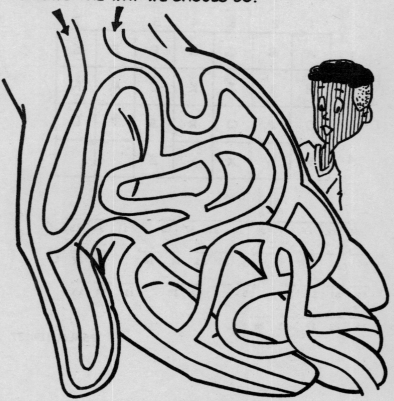

**ALL THINGS ARE IN HIS HAND.
HE IS IN CONTROL OF MY LIFE.**

CODE BUSTER

USE THE CODE CHART BELOW TO COMPLETE THE VERSE. CHOOSE FROM THE LEFT SET OF NUMBERS FIRST. (Eg: 23=J)

	1	2	3	4	5	6	7
1	A	B	C	D	E	F	G
2	H	I	J	K	L	M	N
3	O	P	Q	R	S	T	U
4	V	W	X	Y	Z		

"
— — — — — — — — —   — — —
34 22 17 21 36 15 31 37 35   11 34 15

— — —,   — —   — — — —,   — — —
44 31 37   31   25 31 34 14   11 27 14

— — — —   — — — —   — — —
44 31 37 34   25 11 42 35   11 34 15

— — — — —"
34 22 17 21 36

PSALM 119:137

GOD IS RIGHTEOUS.
HE CANNOT SIN AGAINST ME.

ZANY CODE BUSTER

TO DECODE THIS MYSTERY VERSE, LOOK AT EACH LETTER AND WRITE THE ONE THAT COMES <u>BEFORE</u> IT IN THE ALPHABET.

A B C D E F G H I J K L M N O P Q R
S T U V W X Y Z

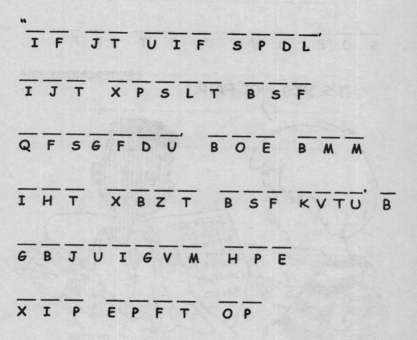

"_ _   _ _   _ _ _   _ _ _ _,
 I F   JT   UIF   SPDL,

_ _ _   _ _ _ _   _ _ _
I J T   X P S L T   B S F

_ _ _ _ _ _,   _ _ _   _ _ _
Q F S G F D U   B O E   B M M

_ _ _   _ _ _ _   _ _ _   _ _ _ _,   _
I H T   X B Z T   B S F   K V T U   B

_ _   _ _ _ _ _ _   _ _ _
G B   J U I G V M   H P E

_ _ _   _ _ _ _   _ _
X I P   E P F T   O P

GOD IS JUST.

CONT'D ON THE NEXT PAGE...

CONT'D FROM THE PREVIOUS PAGE.

__ __ __ __ __ , __ __ __ __ __ __
X S P O H   V Q S J H I U

__ __ __ __ __ __ __ __ __ __ __."
B O E   K V T U   J T   I F

DEUTERONOMY 32:4

IT'S JUST NOT FAIR!

DID IT EVER OCCUR TO YOU THAT IF ONE...STUDIES..?

HE WILL ALWAYS BE FAIR WITH ME.

ZANY CODE BUSTER

USE THE CODE CHART BELOW TO DECODE THE MYSTERY VERSE.

GOD IS LOVE.

CONT'D ON THE NEXT PAGE...

1 JOHN 4:8

HE WANTS TO HELP ME GET THE MOST
OUT OF LIFE.

UNSCRAMBLE AND ANSWER

FIRST, UNSCRAMBLE THE WORDS AND WRITE
THEM IN THE SPACES UNDER EACH WORD. THEN
LIST ALL THE CIRCLED LETTERS BELOW AND
UNSCRAMBLE THEM TO COMPLETE THE
STATEMENT.

"EHT   LEATNER   DGO   SI

___   _____   ___   __

RYOU   EFEGRFU   ADN

____   _____   ___

HUTNADEENR   ERA

_____   ___

HET   GENEIRVTLSA   SARM."

___   _____   _____

DEUTERONOMY 33:27

GOD IS ○○○○○○○.

THE PLAN HE IS WORKING OUT FOR ME
IS EVERLASTING

FINISH THE VERSE

TO FIND OUT WHAT THE VERSE BELOW SAYS, FILL IN THE BLANKS. ALL THE CONSONANTS ARE THERE, SO ALL YOU NEED TO DO IS ADD THE VOWELS.

VOWELS: A E I O U

"__ L__RD, Y__ __ H__V __

S__ __RCH__D M__ __ND Y__ __

KN__W M__. Y__ __. KN__W WH__N __

S__T __ND WH__N __ R__S__; Y__ __

P__RC__ __V__ MY TH__ __GHTS FR__M

__F__R. Y__ __ D__SC__RN MY G__ __NG

__ __T __ND MY LY__NG D__WN;

Y__ __ __RE F__M__L__ __R W__TH

__LL MY W__YS. B__F__R__ __ W__RD

__S __N MY T__NG__ __ __

GOD IS ALL KNOWING.

CONT'D ON THE NEXT PAGE...

CONT'D FROM THE PREVIOUS PAGE.

Y_ _ KN__W _T C __MPL__T__LY,

_ L__RD. Y_ _ H_M M_ _N —

B__H__ND __ND B__F__R_; Y_ _

H__V_ L__D Y_ _ _R H_ND _P_N

M__."

PSALM 139:1-5

HE KNOWS ALL ABOUT ME AND MY SITUATION
AND HOW TO WORK IT OUT FOR GOOD.

123

HIDDEN ALPHABET

FIND AND CIRCLE EVERY LETTER OF THE ALPHABET
THAT HAS BEEN HIDDEN IN THIS PICTURE AND
FINISH THE SENTENCE BELOW.

GOD KNOWS THE WAY
I __ __ __ __ __ GO.

FINISH THE PICTURE

USING THE GRID, DRAW THE PICTURE BELOW ON THE FOLLOWING PAGE.

FROM THE PREVIOUS PAGE, USE THE GRID TO
DRAW THE PICTURE FOR YOURSELF.

UNSCRAMBLE THE VERSE

TO FIND OUT WHAT THE VERSE BELOW SAYS, FILL
IN THE BLANKS. ALL THE VOWELS ARE THERE, SO
ALL YOU NEED TO ADD ARE THE CONSONANTS.

"REWEH NCA I OG OMRF UROY IITSPR? HEWER CAN I
ELFE RFMO OYRU SCPENERE? FI I OG PU OT HET
VNHEESA OYU EAR RTEHE; FI I EMAK YM DBE NI
THE TDESPH, OYU RAE EEHRT. FI I ESRI NO EHT
NIGWS FO ETH WDNA, FI I TELTES NO ETH ARF
IEDS FO HET EAS, VNEE REEHT YRUO NADH WILL
IEGDU EM, UYRO HITRG ADHN LWLI DOHL EM STFA."

"__E__E __A__   I   __O   ___O__

__O U__   ___I__I__?   ___E__E

__A__   I   ___EE   ___O__   __O U__

___E__E___E?   I__   I   __O   U__

__O   ___E   __EA__E___   __O U

A__E   ___E__E;   I__   I   __A__E

__Y   __E__   I__   ___E   __E_____,

__O U   A__E   ___E__E.

CONT'D ON THE NEXT PAGE...

127

I_ _ I _ _I_ E _ O _ _ _ _E _

_ _ I _ _ _ _ _ O _ _ _ E _ _ A _ _ _,

I _ _ I _ _ _ E _ _ _ _ E O _ _ _ _ E

_ _ A _ _ _ I _ E O _ _ _ _ E _ EA,

E _ E _ _ _ _ E _ E _ OU _ _ A _ _

_ _ I _ _ _ _ UI _ E _ E, _ _ OU _

_ _ I _ _ _ _ _ A _ _ _ _ I _ _ _ _ O _ _

_ E _ _ A _ _ _."

PSALM 139:7-10

GOD IS EVERYWHERE.
THERE IS NO PLACE I CAN GO THAT HE
WILL NOT TAKE CARE OF ME.

ZANY CODE BUSTER

USE THE CODE CHART BELOW TO DECODE THE MYSTERY VERSE.

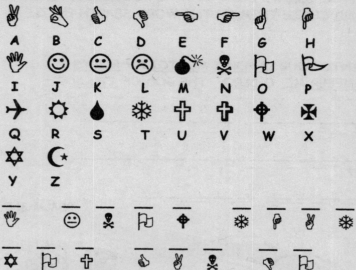

JOB 42:2

GOD IS ALL POWERFUL.
THERE IS NOTHING HE CAN'T DO ON MY
BEHALF.

129

TWICE THE FUN

UNSCRAMBLE THE UNDERLINED WORDS IN THE VERSE BELOW. THEN, ON THE NEXT PAGE, FIND AND CIRCLE THEM IN THE WORD SEARCH PUZZLE.

"INTO YOUR <u>DNHSA</u> I <u>MCMTOI</u> MY <u>RIIPTS</u> : <u>DMEEER</u> ME, O <u>DLRO</u> , THE GOD OF <u>TTHUR</u> ."

_____ _____

_____ _____

_____ _____

PSALM 31:5

CONT'D ON THE NEXT PAGE...

130

```
S  V  H  D  J  R  B  S
L  T  R  U  T  H  G  P
O  S  D  E  H  S  V  I
R  J  B  G  D  N  R  R
D  H  V  N  L  E  D  I
G  R  A  Q  J  S  E  T
B  H  D  S  V  R  H  M
C  O  M  M  I  T  J  D
```

GOD IS TRUTH.
GOD CANNOT LIE TO ME.

AMAZING MAZES

AS YOU GO THROUGH THE MAZE, COLLECT THE LETTERS AND COMPLETE THE VERSE BELOW.

"I THE LORD DO NOT ＿ ＿ ＿ ＿ ＿ ＿ ."

MALACHI 3:6

GOD IS UNCHANGING.

SQUARE GAME

COLOR IN THE AREAS THAT HAVE A SQUARE TO
COMPLETE THE STATEMENT BELOW.

I CAN DEPEND ON __ __ __ !

FILL IN THE BLANKS

WORD LIST:	
FEAR	HOLY
GLORY	WORSHIP
NAME	RIGHTEOUS

"WHO WILL NOT __ __ __ __ YOU, O LORD

AND BRING __ __ __ __ __ TO YOUR __ __ __ __?

FOR YOU ALONE ARE __ __ __ __. ALL

NATIONS WILL COME AND

__ __ __ __ __ __ __ BEFORE YOU, FOR YOUR

__ __ __ __ __ __ __ __ __ ACTS HAVE BEEN

REVEALED."

REVELATION 15:4

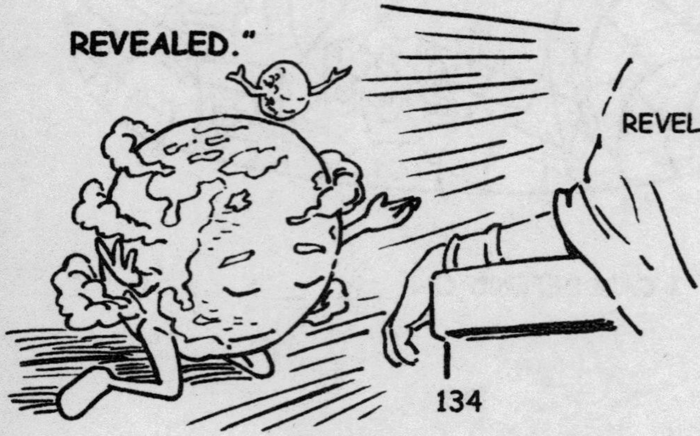

WORD SEARCH

FIND AND CIRCLE THE WORDS BELOW IN THE
WORD SEARCH PUZZLE. LOOK UP, DOWN, FORWARD
AND DIAGONALLY TO SOLVE THIS ONE!

```
C F L X Z L V P K G I J Y Z
P K V G L O R Y F Z X E L C
L F X Z C F G I J Y K T P V
V G A K D P I L Z C X E L F
F L C I X Z P A D G K R J V
V J P K T C F W G D Z N X L
L U F X Z H G S D K C A P V
C S V P K G F D J Z X L L F
F T Z X L D J U Y G K P V C
X V C P K G J Y L D F L Z X
R O C K L X Z D C G K P V F
Z V P K F G J Y Z J D C X L
C F L X G K P V Z F A R M S
Z V P D W Z Y J G K X L F C
X J K L F C R E F U G E P V
```

GLORY
LAWS
ROCK
FAITHFUL

JUST
ETERNAL
REFUGE
ARMS

135

CODE BUSTER

USE THE CODE CHART BELOW TO COMPLETE THE VERSE. CHOOSE FROM THE LEFT SET OF NUMBERS FIRST. (Eg: 23=J)

	1	2	3	4	5	6	7
1	A	B	C	D	E	F	G
2	H	I	J	K	L	M	N
3	O	P	Q	R	S	T	U
4	V	W	X	Y	Z		

"
24 27 31 42   36 21 15 34 15 16 31 34 15

36 21 11 36   36 21 15   25 31 34 14

44 31 37 34   17 31 14   22 35   17 31 14 ;

21 15   22 35   36 21 15   16 11 22 36 21 -

16 37 25   17 31 14

CONT'D ON THE NEXT PAGE...

. CONT'D FROM THE PREVIOUS PAGE.

24 15 15 32 22 27 17   21 22 35

13 31 41 15 27 11 27 36   31 16   25 31 41 15

36 31   11   36 21 31 37 35 11 27 14

17 15 27 15 34 11 36 22 31 27 35   31 16

36 21 31 35 15   42 21 31   25 31 41 15

21 22 26   11 27 14   24 15 15 32   21 22 35

13 31 26 26 11 27 14 35 . "

DEUTERONOMY 7:9

GOD IS HOLY.
HE WILL BE HOLY IN ALL HE DOES.

•DOT 2 DOT•

CONNECT THE DOTS

WHEN YOU PRAY, YOU CAN ALWAYS COUNT ON GOD'S CHARACTER!

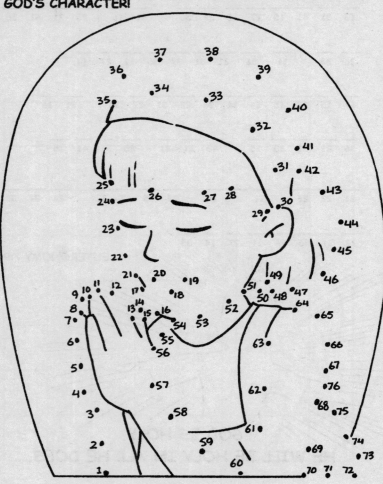

138

FINISH THE PICTURE

USING THE GRID, COMPLETE THE PICTURE BY DUPLICATING THE FINISHED HALF ONTO THE UNFINISHED AREA. ONE SQUARE HAS ALREADY BEEN STARTED FOR YOU.

JESUS IS NOBLE OF CHARACTER.
JESUS, THE LION OF JUDAH!

COLOR THE SCROLL
GOD'S CHARACTER

GOD IS KING OF THE UNIVERSE

GOD IS RIGHTEOUS

GOD IS JUST

GOD IS LOVE

GOD IS ETERNAL

GOD IS ALL KNOWING

GOD IS EVERYWHERE

GOD IS ALL POWERFUL

GOD IS TRUTH

GOD IS UNCHANGEABLE

GOD IS FAITHFUL

GOD IS HOLY

COLOR THE PICTURE

WHO I AM IN CHRIST...
FORGIVEN!

UNSCRAMBLE AND ANSWER

FIRST, UNSCRAMBLE THE WORDS AND WRITE THEM
IN THE SPACES UNDER EACH WORD. THEN LIST ALL
THE CIRCLED LETTERS BELOW AND UNSCRAMBLE
THEM TO COMPLETE THE STATEMENT.

"RRETFEOEH, CINSE EW EHVA

_____ ___○_ __ _○__

ENBE TFIDEJISU GRUHTOH

____ _____ _____

THFIA, EW EVHA CPEAE TIWH

_____ __ __○__ _____ ____

ODG UTGHORH URO ROLD

____ _____ ___ ____

SUEJS RCITHS."

○____ ○____

ROMANS 5:1

I HAVE ○○○○○ WITH GOD.

142

FILL IN THE BLANKS

WORD LIST:

BLAMELESS   SIGHT
WORLD   CREATION
HOLY   CHOSE

"FOR HE _ _ _ _ _ US IN HIM BEFORE

THE _ _ _ _ _ _ _ _ OF THE

_ _ _ _ _ TO BE _ _ _ _ AND

_ _ _ _ _ _ _ _ _ IN HIS

_ _ _ _ _ ."

EPHESIANS 1:4

I AM ACCEPTED BY GOD!

UNSCRAMBLE THE VERSE

TO FIND OUT WHAT THE VERSE BELOW SAYS, FILL IN THE BLANKS. ALL THE VOWELS ARE THERE, SO ALL YOU NEED TO ADD ARE THE CONSONANTS.

"ETY OT LAL OWH EEVRIEC MHI OT SEHTO HOW LVEEBIE NI SHI EAMN, EH EVGA HET HRTIG OT OEMBOC RIEHNCLD FO OGD. . ."

"_E_ _O A__ __O

_E_EI_E _I_, _O __O_E

__O _E_IE_E I_ _I_

_A_E, _E _A_E __E

_I___ _O _E_O_E

__I___E_ O_ _O_."

JOHN 1:12

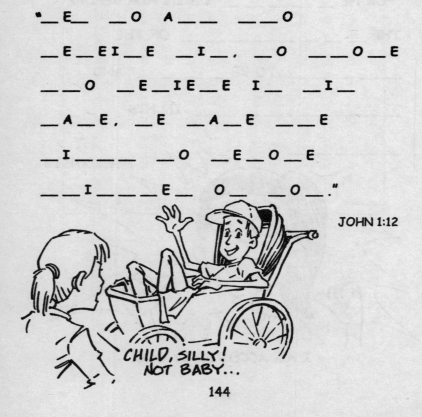

CHILD, SILLY!
NOT BABY...

WORD SEARCH

FIND AND CIRCLE THE WORDS BELOW IN THE
WORD SEARCH PUZZLE. LOOK UP, DOWN, FORWARD
AND DIAGONALLY TO SOLVE THIS ONE!

B	H	L	G	K	C	F	T	J	D	Q	Z	Y	V
D	W	O	R	S	H	I	P	B	K	C	L	F	G
C	F	G	L	T	C	L	D	Z	J	V	E	W	X
H	Q	B	J	Y	K	V	F	G	D	V	C	T	L
I	G	D	L	Y	T	W	J	K	I	B	Z	Q	Y
L	F	K	Z	H	D	C	G	E	T	J	L	V	B
D	J	Q	G	Y	B	R	C	T	F	C	J	K	G
R	L	I	K	G	P	E	A	C	E	F	D	B	O
E	S	B	C	F	R	A	L	G	K	J	Z	T	D
N	K	D	T	J	Q	T	B	F	Y	C	F	D	L
B	Z	F	L	C	K	I	G	D	A	V	T	W	J
Q	Y	V	T	D	G	O	L	K	B	I	C	Q	F
J	L	K	Z	C	F	N	J	T	Y	D	T	G	K
C	T	F	B	G	L	D	K	F	J	C	Z	H	T
K	E	T	E	R	N	A	L	L	G	F	J	B	C

PEACE
FAITH
RECEIVE
HOLY
ETERNAL

SIGHT
CHILDREN
CREATION
GOD
WORSHIP

LOOK-ALIKES

FIND AND CIRCLE TWELVE DIFFERENCES IN THE
TWO PICTURES BELOW.

FINISH THE VERSE

TO FIND OUT WHAT THE VERSE BELOW SAYS, FILL
IN THE BLANKS. ALL THE CONSONANTS ARE THERE,
SO ALL YOU NEED TO DO IS ADD THE VOWELS.

VOWELS: A E I O U

"D _ N'T Y _ _ KN _ W TH _ T

Y _ _ Y _ _ RS _ LV _ S _ R _

G _ D'S T _ MPL _ _ ND TH _ T

G _ D'S SP _ R _ T L _ V _ S

_ N Y _ _ ?"

1 CORINTHIANS 3:16

I KNOW HE'S IN HERE...
THERE'S GOTTA BE SOMETHING WRONG WITH YOUR PROGRAMMING!

WELLL... I'LL KEEP LOOKING...

ACME X-RAY VIEWER

I HAVE THE HOLY SPIRIT INSIDE ME!

ZANY CODE BUSTER

USE THE CODE CHART BELOW TO DECODE THE MYSTERY VERSE.

HMMMM...
THERE HAS TO
BE A MORE...
PRACTICAL WAY!

CONT'D ON THE NEXT PAGE...

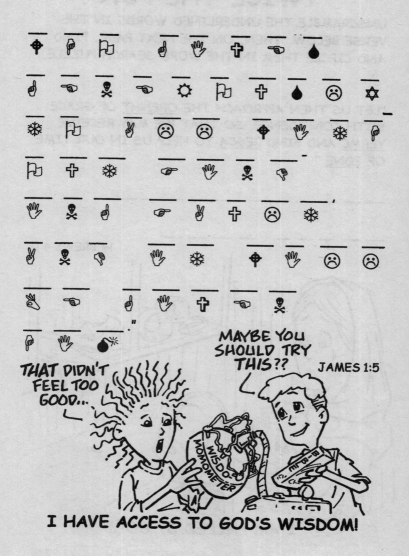

TWICE THE FUN

UNSCRAMBLE THE UNDERLINED WORDS IN THE VERSE BELOW. THEN, ON THE NEXT PAGE, FIND AND CIRCLE THEM IN THE WORD SEARCH PUZZLE.

"LET US THEN APPROACH THE <u>ORENHT</u> OF GRACE WITH CONFIDENCE, SO THAT WE MAY RECEIVE <u>YERMC</u> AND FIND <u>REGCA</u> TO HELP US IN OUR TIME OF <u>EDNE</u>."

__ __ __ __ __ __   __ __ __ __ __

__ __ __ __ __   __ __ __ __

HEBREWS 4:16

I AM HELPED BY GOD!

CONT'D ON THE NEXT PAGE...

```
S  Q  D  W  G  L  Z  M
K  T  H  R  O  N  E  G
F  R  N  P  Y  C  B  M
A  L  H  E  A  R  F  E
P  X  O  R  D  J  N  R
R  N  G  K  F  Q  V  C
I  F  P  S  N  R  D  Y
N  E  E  D  R  F  P  J
```

HIDDEN ALPHABET

FIND AND CIRCLE EVERY LETTER OF THE ALPHABET THAT HAS BEEN HIDDEN IN THIS PICTURE AND FINISH THE SENTENCE BELOW.

I RECEIVE __ __ __ __ __ BECAUSE OF GOD'S GRACE.

AMAZING MAZES

FIND THE WAY TO THE THRONE OF GRACE.

CODE BUSTER

USE THE CODE CHART BELOW TO COMPLETE THE VERSE. CHOOSE FROM THE LEFT SET OF NUMBERS FIRST. (Eg: 23=J)

	1	2	3	4	5	6	7
1	A	B	C	D	E	F	G
2	H	I	J	K	L	M	N
3	O	P	Q	R	S	T	U
4	V	W	X	Y	Z		

"___ ___ ___   ___ ___ ___ ___   ___ ___   ___ ___ ___ ___
27 31 36   31 27 25 44   22 35   36 21 22 35

___ ___ '   ___ ___ ___   ___ ___   ___ ___ ___ ___
35 31   12 37 36   42 15   11 25 35 31

___ ___ ___ ___ ___ ___ ___   ___ ___   ___ ___ ___
34 15 23 31 22 13 15   22 27   17 31 14

___ ___ ___ ___ ___ ___ ___   ___ ___ ___   ___ ___ ___ ___
36 21 34 31 37 17 21   31 37 34   25 31 34 14

___ ___ ___ ___ ___   ___ ___ ___ ___ ___ ___ .
23 15 35 37 35   13 21 34 22 35 36

CONT'D ON THE NEXT PAGE...

CONT'D FROM THE PREVIOUS PAGE.

——— ——— ——— ——— ——— ——— ———   ——— ——— ——— ———
36 21 34 31 37 17 21   42 21 31 26

——— ———   ——— ——— ——— ———   ——— ——— ———
42 15   21 11 41 15   27 31 · 42

——— ——— ——— ——— ——— ——— ——— ———
34 15 13 15 22 41 15 14

——— ——— ——— ——— ——— ——— ——— ——— ——— ——— ——— ——— ——— .”
34 15 13 31 27 13 22 25 22 11 36 22 31 27

HEY... WHAT IN THE WORLD DOES... REC... RECO... RECON-WHATEVER MEAN...?

ROMANS 5:11

"RECONCILE"? IT MEANS TO BE MADE "FRIENDS WITH AGAIN". SO WE'RE MADE FRIENDS AGAIN WITH GOD!

HMMPH... COOL!

CHILDREN BIBLE

I AM RECONCILED TO GOD!

155

ZANY CODE BUSTER

TO DECODE THIS MYSTERY VERSE, LOOK AT EACH LETTER AND WRITE THE ONE THAT COMES <u>BEFORE</u> IT IN THE ALPHABET.

A B C D E F G H I J K L M N O P Q R
S T U V W X Y Z

" __ __ __ __ __ __ __ __ __ ' __ __ __ __
    U I F S F G P S F   U I F S F

__ __ __ __ __ __ __ __ __ __ __ __ -
J T   O P X   O P   D P O E F N

__ __ __ __ __ __ __ __ __ __ __ __
O B U J P O   G P S   U I P T F

__ __
X I P

CONT'D ON THE NEXT PAGE...

156

‾ ‾ ‾   ‾ ‾   ‾ ‾ ‾ ‾ ‾ ‾
B S F   J O   D I S J T U

‾ ‾ ‾ ‾ ‾ ."
K F T V T

WHAT ABOUT, CON... CON-DEM-NATION? WHAT DOES THAT MEAN?

TO BE CONVICTED AS GUILTY. TO BE JUDGED... TO BE BLAMED, CRITICIZED, DOOMED, SEN...

ROMANS 8:1

OKAY, OKAY! I GET IT...

WOW! THANKS TO JESUS... THAT'LL NEVER HAPPEN TO US!

WAY COOLER EVEN!

THERE IS NO CONDEMNATION FOR ME!

PICTURE FRAMES

WHAT COULD THE PICTURE BE?

DRAW EXACTLY WHAT IS IN EACH NUMBERED
FRAME AT THE TOP OF THE PAGE INTO EACH FRAME
OF THE SAME NUMBER IN THE GRID BELOW.

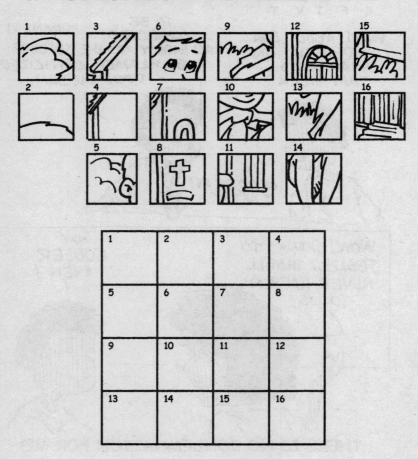

•DOT 2 DOT•

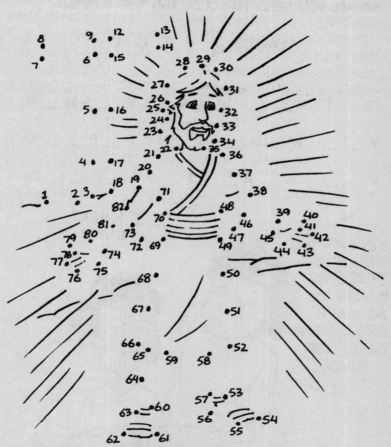

THERE IS *NO* CONDEMNATION FOR THOSE WHO ARE IN JESUS CHRIST!

FINISH THE VERSE

TO FIND OUT WHAT THE VERSE BELOW SAYS, FILL IN THE BLANKS. ALL THE CONSONANTS ARE THERE, SO ALL YOU NEED TO DO IS ADD THE VOWELS.

VOWELS: A E I O U

"B _ T Y _ _ _ W _ R _ W _ SH _ D,

y _ _ _ W _ R _ S _ NCT _ F _ _ D,

y _ _ _ W _ R _ J _ ST _ F _ _ D

_ N

BEFORE YOU EVEN ASK... "JUSTIFIED" MEANS TO BE MADE FREE FROM GUILT OR BLAME

I KNEW THAT!

CONT'D ON THE NEXT PAGE...

CONT'D FROM THE PREVIOUS PAGE.

TH__ N__M__ __F TH__
L__RD J__S__S CHR__ST
__ND BY TH__ SP__R__T __F
__ __R G__D."

1 CORINTHIANS 6:11

WORD SEARCH

CROSS OUT EVERY LETTER THAT APPEARS FOUR
TIMES IN THE PUZZLE TO FIND THE WORD THAT
COMPLETES THE SENTENCE.

```
D O B T N R K S
R F J Z P C G X
S K B G X H X B
N E C H D F J P
J P Z X V B Z S
H F N R T T G C
K Z G C S P F H
L D T J K N R D
```

BECAUSE OF HIS GREAT __ __ __ __ FOR US,
JESUS PAID THE PRICE FOR ALL OUR SINS!

162

LOOK-ALIKES

FIND AND CIRCLE TEN DIFFERENCES IN THE TWO
PICTURES BELOW.

CODE BUSTER

USE THE CODE CHART BELOW TO COMPLETE THE
VERSE. CHOOSE FROM THE LEFT SET OF NUMBERS
FIRST. (Eg: 23=J)

	1	2	3	4	5	6	7
1	A	B	C	D	E	F	G
2	H	I	J	K	L	M	N
3	O	P	Q	R	S	T	U
4	V	W	X	Y	Z		

"___ ___ ___   ___ ___ ___ ___   ___ ___ ___   ___ ___ ___
 17 31 14   26 11 14 15   21 22 26   42 21 31

___ ___ ___   ___ ___   ___ ___ ___   ___ ___   ___ ___
21 11 14   27 31   35 22 27   36 31   12 15

___ ___ ___   ___ ___ ___   ___ ___ ,   ___ ___
35 22 27   16 31 34   37 35   35 31

___ ___ ___ ___   ___ ___   ___ ___ ___
36 21 11 36   22 27   21 22 26

CONT'D ON THE NEXT PAGE...

— 42 15 — 26 22 17 21 36 — 12 15 13 31 26 15

— 36 21 15 — 34 22 17 21 36 15 31 37 35 -

27 15 35 35 — 31 16 — 17 31 14 — ."

2 CORINTHIANS 5:21

JUST SO YOU KNOW...
"RIGHTEOUSNESS" ALSO
MEANS TO BE "FREE OF
GUILT"...TO BE SEEN
AS RIGHTEOUS IN
GOD'S EYES!

MMPHH...
MMMHH...
MMPHH...
MMPHH

I HAVE HIS RIGHTEOUSNESS!

FILL IN THE BLANKS

WORD LIST:

APPEAL	AMBASSADORS
CHRIST'S	WE
GOD	US

"_ _ ARE THEREFORE _ _ _ _ _ _'_

_ _ _ _ _ _ _ _ _ _ _, AS

THOUGH _ _ _ WERE MAKING HIS

_ _ _ _ _ _ _ THROUGH _ _ ."

2 CORINTHIANS 5:20

I AM GOD'S REPRESENTATIVE!

FINISH THE PICTURE

USING THE GRID, COMPLETE THE PICTURE BY
DUPLICATING THE FINISHED HALF ONTO THE
UNFINISHED AREA. ONE SQUARE HAS ALREADY
BEEN STARTED FOR YOU.

TWICE THE FUN

UNSCRAMBLE THE UNDERLINED WORDS IN THE VERSE BELOW. THEN, ON THE NEXT PAGE, FIND AND CIRCLE THEM IN THE WORD SEARCH PUZZLE.

"IF WE <u>EFCSOSN</u> OUR <u>SNSI</u>, HE IS <u>FFLUIAHT</u> AND <u>SUTJ</u> AND WILL <u>VGEROFI</u> US OUR SINS AND <u>RPIYFU</u> US FROM ALL UNRIGHTEOUSNESS."

_____ _____

_____ _____

_____ _____

1 JOHN 1:9

CONT'D ON THE NEXT PAGE...

```
L J U S T B E P
S C H M I V W U
I S B K I N L R
N M X G C H S I
S H R W S T K F
B O L C V R B Y
F A I T H F U L
L C O N F E S S
```

I HAVE TO ADMIT... THIS WAY IS BETTER!

I AM COMPLETELY FORGIVEN!

ZANY CODE BUSTER

USE THE CODE CHART BELOW TO DECODE THE MYSTERY VERSE.

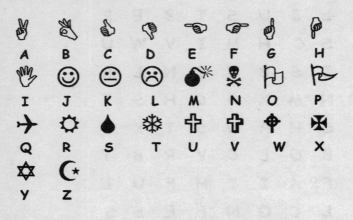

A   B   C   D   E   F   G   H

I   J   K   L   M   N   O   P

Q   R   S   T   U   V   W   X

Y   Z

CONT'D ON THE NEXT PAGE...

FINISH THE PICTURE

USING THE GRID, DRAW THE PICTURE BELOW ON
THE FOLLOWING PAGE.

GOD'S LOVE IS SO AWESOME!

FROM THE PREVIOUS PAGE, USE THE GRID TO DRAW THE PICTURE FOR YOURSELF.

ZANY CODE BUSTER

TO DECODE THIS MYSTERY VERSE, LOOK AT EACH LETTER AND WRITE THE ONE THAT COMES <u>BEFORE</u> IT IN THE ALPHABET.

A B C D E F G H I J K L M N O P Q R
S T U V W X Y Z

"__ __ __ __ __ __ __ __ __ __ __ __
   J I B W F   M P W F E   Z P V

__ __ __ __ __ __ __ __ __ __ __ __-
 X J U I   B O   F W F S M B T U

__ __ __ __ __ __."
 J O H   M P W F

JEREMIAH 31:3

I AM TENDERLY LOVED!

UNSCRAMBLE THE VERSE

TO FIND OUT WHAT THE VERSE BELOW SAYS, FILL IN THE BLANKS. ALL THE VOWELS ARE THERE, SO ALL YOU NEED TO ADD ARE THE CONSONANTS.

"OFR EW REA OT OGD HET OAMRA FO ITHCRS MAGNO HETSO HWO EAR NBIGE VADSE NAD TESHO HOW REA HGIIPRESN."

" __ O __   __ E A __ E   __ O   __ O __

__ __ E   A __ O __ A   O __   __ __ __ I __ __

A __ O __ __   __ __ O __ E   __ __ O   A __ E

__ E I __ __   __ A __ E __   A __ __

__ __ O __ E   __ __ O   A __ E   __ E __ I __ __ -

I __ __ . "

— 2 CORINTHIANS 2:15

I AM A SWEET SMELL OF CHRIST TO GOD!

175

FINISH THE VERSE

TO FIND OUT WHAT THE VERSE BELOW SAYS, FILL IN THE BLANKS. ALL THE CONSONANTS ARE THERE, SO ALL YOU NEED TO DO IS ADD THE VOWELS.

VOWELS: A E I O U

"F__R W__ __R__ TH__
T__MPL__ __F TH__ L__V__NG
G__D."

2 CORINTHIANS 6:16

YOU KNOW, HAREEM...
WE *REALLY* NEED
TO TALK...

I AM THE TEMPLE OF GOD!

CODE BUSTER

USE THE CODE CHART BELOW TO COMPLETE THE VERSE. CHOOSE FROM THE LEFT SET OF NUMBERS FIRST. (Eg: 23=J)

	1	2	3	4	5	6	7
1	A	B	C	D	E	F	G
2	H	I	J	K	L	M	N
3	O	P	Q	R	S	T	U
4	V	W	X	Y	Z		

"
―― ―― ―― ―― ―― ―― ―― ―― ―― ―― ――
12 37 36   27 31 42   21 15   21 11 35

―― ―― ―― ―― ―― ―― ―― ―― ―― ―― ―― ―― ――
34 15 13 31 27 13 22 25 15 14   44 31 37

―― ―― ―― ―― ―― ―― ―― , ―― ―― ―― ―― -
12 44   13 21 34 22 35 36   35   32 21 44

―― ―― ―― ―― ―― ―― ―― ―― ――
35 22 13 11 25   12 31 14 44

CONT'D ON THE NEXT PAGE...

___ ___ ___ ___ ___ ___ ___   ___ ___ ___ ___ ___
36   21   34   31   37   17   21   14   15   11   36   21

___ ___   ___ ___ ___ ___ ___ ___ ___   ___ ___ ___
36   31   32   34   15   35   15   27   36   44   31   37

___ ___ ___ ___   ___ ___   ___ ___ ___   ___ ___ ___ ___ ___ ___ ;
21   31   25   44   22   27   21   22   35   35   22   17   21   36

___ ___ ___ ___ ___ ___ ___   ___ ___ ___ ___ ___ ___ ___
42   22   36   21   31   37   36   12   25   15   26   22   35   21

___ ___ ___   ___ ___ ___ ___   ___ ___ ___ ___
11   27   14   16   34   15   15   16   34   31   26

___ ___ ___ ___ ___ ___ ___ ___ ___ ___ ."
11   13   13   37   35   11   36   22   31   27

COLOSSIANS 1:22

I CAN'T SEEM TO FIND MY CHOCO-CANDY-CARAMEL-FRUITY-BEAR PUFFS!?

WELL... EH-HMMPH... DON'T BLAME ME!

I AM BLAMELESS AND BEYOND REPROACH!

COLOR THE PICTURE

ATTITUDE MAKES THE DIFFERENCE!

MY DAILY ATTITUDE ACTION PLAN

ZANY CODE BUSTER

USE THE CODE CHART BELOW TO DECODE THE MYSTERY VERSE.

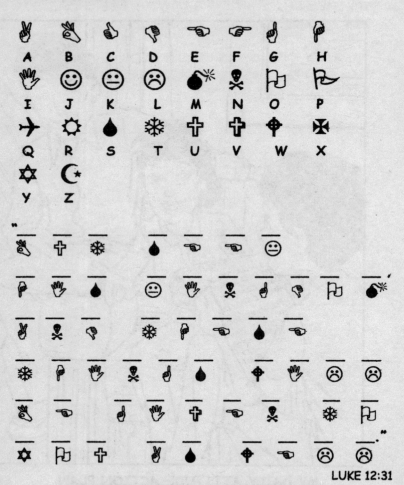

LUKE 12:31

I WILL TALK TO GOD EVERY DAY

UNSCRAMBLE THE VERSE

TO FIND OUT WHAT THE VERSE BELOW SAYS, FILL
IN THE BLANKS. ALL THE VOWELS ARE THERE, SO
ALL YOU NEED TO ADD ARE THE CONSONANTS.

"MMITOC UYRO SWYA OT EHT RODL; UTTRS NI
IHM DAN EH LLWI... EMKA ROYU TEEHSRSIGUOSN
NIHES EILK HET WDAN."

"_ O _ _ I _   _ O U _   _ A _ _   _ O

_ _ E   _ O _ _;   _ _ U _ _   I _

_ I _   A _ _   _ E   _ I _ _...

_ A _ E   _ O U _   _ I _ _ _ E O U _-

_ E _ _   _ _ I _ E   _ I _ E   _ _ E

_ A _ _."

PSALM 37:5-6

I WILL COMMIT MY WAYS TO THE LORD

181

FINISH THE PICTURE

USING THE GRID, DRAW THE PICTURE BELOW ON
THE FOLLOWING PAGE.

"ALTITUDE" DEPENDS ON YOUR ATTITUDE!

FROM THE PREVIOUS PAGE, USE THE GRID TO
DRAW THE PICTURE FOR YOURSELF.

FINISH THE VERSE

TO FIND OUT WHAT THE VERSE BELOW SAYS, FILL
IN THE BLANKS. ALL THE CONSONANTS ARE THERE,
SO ALL YOU NEED TO DO IS ADD THE VOWELS.

VOWELS: A E I O U

"TH__S __S TH__ D__Y TH__

L__RD H__S M__D__; L__T

__S R__J__ __C__ __ND B__

GL__D __N __T."

PSALM 118:24

I WILL MAKE TODAY MY BEST DAY...!

EEW...!

I WILL MAKE TODAY MY BEST DAY

184

CODE BUSTER

USE THE CODE CHART BELOW TO COMPLETE THE VERSE. CHOOSE FROM THE LEFT SET OF NUMBERS FIRST. (Eg: 23=J)

	1	2	3	4	5	6	7
1	A	B	C	D	E	F	G
2	H	I	J	K	L	M	N
3	O	P	Q	R	S	T	U
4	V	W	X	Y	Z		

"
‾‾ ‾‾ ‾‾ ‾‾ ‾‾ ‾‾ ‾‾ ‾‾
42 21 11 36 15 41 15 34

‾‾ ‾‾ ‾‾ ‾‾ ‾‾ ‾‾ ‾‾ ,   ‾‾ ‾‾ ‾‾ ‾‾ ‾‾ ‾‾ ‾‾
21 11 32 32 15 27 35   13 31 27 14 37 13 36

‾‾ ‾‾ ‾‾ ‾‾ ‾‾ ‾‾ ‾‾ ‾‾ ‾‾ ‾‾   ‾‾ ‾‾   ‾‾
44 31 37 34 35 15 25 41 15 35   22 27   11

‾‾ ‾‾ ‾‾ ‾‾ ‾‾ ‾‾   ‾‾ ‾‾ ‾‾ ‾‾ ‾‾ ‾‾   ‾‾ ‾‾
26 11 27 27 15 34   42 31 34 36 21 44   31 16

‾‾ ‾‾ ‾‾   ‾‾ ‾‾ ‾‾ ‾‾ ‾‾ ‾‾   ‾‾ ‾‾
36 21 15   17 31 35 32 15 25   31 16

‾‾ ‾‾ ‾‾ ‾‾ ‾‾ ‾‾ . "
13 21 34 22 35 36

PHILIPPIANS 1:27

185

TWICE THE FUN

UNSCRAMBLE THE UNDERLINED WORDS IN THE VERSE BELOW. THEN, ON THE NEXT PAGE, FIND AND CIRCLE THEM IN THE WORD SEARCH PUZZLE.

"BE <u>NIDK</u> AND COMPASSIONATE TO <u>EON</u> ANOTHER, FORGIVING EACH OTHER, <u>SJTU</u> AS IN <u>SRIHTC</u> GOD <u>VRAFGEO</u> YOU."

___ ____ ____ ____

_____ _____ _____

EPHESIANS 4:32

CONT'D ON THE NEXT PAGE...

CONT'D FROM THE PREVIOUS PAGE.

```
D  F  R  C  K  B  H  R
K  F  B  H  C  L  Z  J
R  C  O  N  E  K  F  U
B  C  H  R  I  S  T  S
K  H  R  F  G  C  K  T
Z  I  K  C  B  A  F  R
F  R  N  H  K  L  V  C
Y  C  K  D  F  R  B  E
```

I WILL BE KIND TO OTHERS

PICTURE FRAMES
WHAT COULD THE PICTURE BE?

DRAW EXACTLY WHAT IS IN EACH NUMBERED
FRAME AT THE TOP OF THE PAGE INTO EACH FRAME
OF THE SAME NUMBER IN THE GRID BELOW.

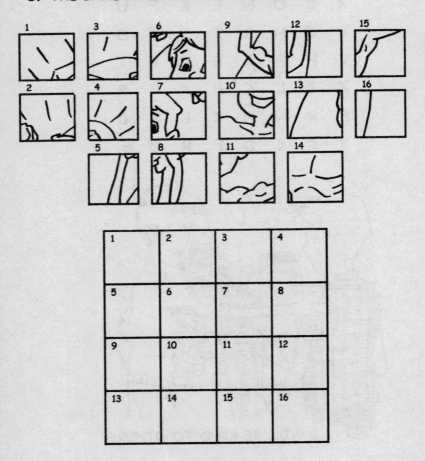

ZANY CODE BUSTER

TO DECODE THIS MYSTERY VERSE, LOOK AT EACH LETTER AND WRITE THE ONE THAT COMES <u>BEFORE</u> IT IN THE ALPHABET.

A B C D E F G H I J K L M N O P Q R
S T U V W X Y Z

" _ _ _ _ _ _ _ _ _ _ -
  J   D B O   E P   F W F S Z

_ _ _ _ _ _ _ _ _ _
U I J O H   U I S P V H I

_ _ _ _ _ _ _ _ _ _ _
I J N   X I P   H J W F T   N F

_ _ _ _ _ _ _ _ ."
T U S F O H U I

PHILIPPIANS 4:13

I WILL DO WHAT I'M ASKED WITHOUT
COMPLAINT

189

UNSCRAMBLE THE VERSE

TO FIND OUT WHAT THE VERSE BELOW SAYS, FILL IN THE BLANKS. ALL THE VOWELS ARE THERE, SO ALL YOU NEED TO ADD ARE THE CONSONANTS.

"EB VYRE FCLAERU, ETNH, WHO OUY EVIL—TON SA WUESIN TUB SA EIWS, NGIKAM HET TOMS FO RYEEV NTIYURTPOPO, SEBCEUA ETH SDYA RAE LIVE."

"_ E _ E _ _ _ _ A _ E _ U _ ,

_ _ E _ , _ O _ _ O U _ I _ E —

_ O _ A _ U _ _ I _ E _ U _ A _

_ I _ E , _ A _ I _ _ _ _ E

_ O _ _ O _ E _ E _ _ O _ _ O _ -

_ U _ I _ _ , _ E _ A U _ E _ _ E

_ A _ _ A _ E E _ I _ . "

EPHESIANS 5:15-16

I WILL MAKE THE MOST OF EVERY OPPORTUNITY

190

MULTIPLE CHOICE

CIRCLE THE CORRECT ANSWER.

1. WE SHOULD PUT OUR TRUST IN:
   - A. MONEY
   - B. THE LORD
   - C. FRIENDS

2. WHAT MUST WE SEEK TO BE GIVEN ALL THINGS?
   - A. A JOB
   - B. A RAISE IN OUR ALLOWANCE
   - C. GOD'S KINGDOM

3. EVERYONE WHO HAS WILL BE GIVEN:

   MATTHEW 25:29

   - A. A REALLY COOL BIKE
   - B. MORE, AND HE WILL HAVE AN ABUNDANCE
   - C. NOTHING! YOUR ROOM'S TOO CROWDED ANYWAYS!

I WILL USE MY TALENTS EVERY DAY

ZANY CODE BUSTER

USE THE CODE CHART BELOW TO DECODE THE
MYSTERY VERSE.

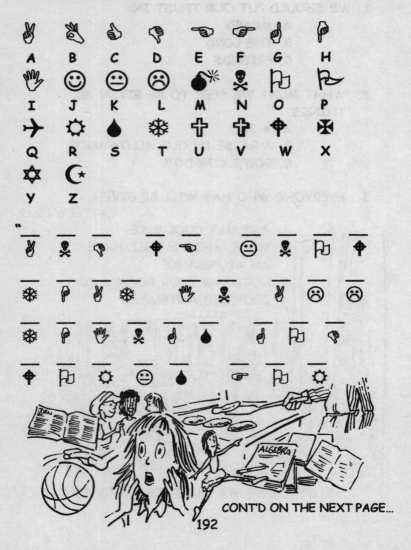

A B C D E F G H

I J K L M N O P

Q R S T U V W X

Y Z

CONT'D ON THE NEXT PAGE...

ROMANS 8:28

I WILL TRUST GOD TO WORK EVERYTHING OUT

FILL IN THE BLANKS

WORD LIST:

HELPFUL	BENEFIT
NEEDS	UNWHOLESOME
ACCORDING	LISTEN
TALK	MOUTHS

" DO NOT LET ANY _ _ _ _ _ _ _ -

_ _ _ _   _ _ _ _ COME OUT OF YOUR

_ _ _ _ _ _ _ , BUT ONLY WHAT IS

_ _ _ _ _ _ _ _ FOR BUILDING OTHERS

UP

HEY... YA' DOIN' THOSE STUPID DRAWINGS AGAIN..?

CONT'D ON THE NEXT PAGE...

CONT'D FROM THE PREVIOUS PAGE.

_ _ _ _ _ _ _ _ _ _ TO THEIR

_ _ _ _ _ _ , THAT IT MAY _ _ _ _ -

_ _ _ THOSE WHO _ _ _ _ _ _ ."

EPHESIANS 4:29

I WILL ENCOURAGE OTHERS TO BE ALL GOD
CREATED THEM TO BE

CODE BUSTER

USE THE CODE CHART BELOW TO COMPLETE THE VERSE. CHOOSE FROM THE LEFT SET OF NUMBERS FIRST. (Eg: 23=J)

	1	2	3	4	5	6	7
1	A	B	C	D	E	F	G
2	H	I	J	K	L	M	N
3	O	P	Q	R	S	T	U
4	V	W	X	Y	Z		

"__ __   __ __ __   __ __   __ __ __ __ __ __ __
 14 31   27 31 36   12 15   11 27 43 22 31 37 35

__ __ __ __ __   __ __ __ __ __ __ __ __ ,
11 12 31 37 36   11 27 44 36 21 22 27 17

__ __ __   __ __   __ __ __ __ __ __ __ __ __ __ ,
12 37 36   22 27   15 41 15 34 44 36 21 22 27 17

__ __   __ __ __ __ __ __
12 44   32 34 11 44 15 34

CONT'D ON THE NEXT PAGE...

___ ___ ___   ___ ___ ___ ___ ___ ___ ___ ___,   ___ ___ ___ ___
11 27 14   32 15 36 22 36 22 31 27   42 22 36 21

___ ___ ___ ___ ___ ___ ___ ___ ___ ___ ___ ___,
36 21 11 27 24 35 17 22 41 22 27 17

___ ___ ___ ___ ___ ___ ___   ___ ___ ___ ___
32 34 15 35 15 27 36   44 31 37 34

___ ___ ___ ___ ___ ___ ___ ___   ___ ___ ___   ___ ___ ___."
34 15 33 37 15 35 36 35   36 31   17 31 14

PHILIPPIANS 4:6

I WILL NOT PANIC...I WILL PRAY

197

COLOR THE COMIC

CONT'D ON THE NEXT PAGE...

CONT'D ON THE NEXT PAGE...

199

ANSWER PAGES

FINISH THE VERSE

FINISH THE VERSE BY MATCHING THEM WITH THE PHRASES ON THE FOLLOWING PAGE

1 "IN THE BEGINNING GOD CREATED..."

   "_THE HEAVENS AND THE EARTH._"

                     GENESIS 1:1

2 "AND GOD SAID 'LET THERE BE LIGHT.'"

   "_AND THERE WAS LIGHT._"

                     GENESIS 1:3

3 "AND GOD SAID 'LET THERE BE AN EXPANSE BETWEEN...'"

   "_THE WATERS TO SEPERATE WATER FROM WATER_"

                     GENESIS 1:6

4 "SO GOD MADE AN EXPANSE AND SEPARATED..."
   "_THE WATER UNDER THE EXPANSE FROM_
   THE WATER ABOVE IT."

                     GENESIS 1:7

5 "AND IT WAS SO GOD CALLED THE..."

   EXPANSE SKY.

6 "AND GOD SAID 'LET THE WATER UNDER THE SKY...'"
   "_BE GATHERED TO ONE PLACE_
   AND LET DRY GROUND APPEAR."

                     GENESIS 1:9

2

FINISH THE VERSE

TO FIND OUT WHAT THE VERSE BELOW SAYS FILL IN THE BLANKS. ALL THE CONSONANTS ARE THERE SO ALL YOU NEED TO DO IS ADD THE VOWELS

VOWELS A E I O U

G O D   C A L L E D   T H E   D A Y

G R O U N D   "L A N D"   A N D   T H E

G A T H E R E D   W A T E R S   H E

C A L L E D   "S E A S"   A N D   G O D

S A W   T H A T   I T   W A S

G O O D"

GENESIS 1:10

4

FILL IN THE BLANKS

WORDLIST

VEGETATION	SEED
LAND	TREES
THEIR	KINDS
PLANTS	FRUIT

"THEN GOD SAID 'LET THE _L A N D_

PRODUCE _V E G E T A T I O N_

SEED-BEARING _P L A N T S_ AND

_T R E E S_ ON THE LAND THAT BEAR

_F R U I T_ WITH _S E E D_ IN IT

ACCORDING TO _T H E I R_ VARIOUS

KINDS'"

                     GENESIS 1:11

5

TWICE THE FUN

UNSCRAMBLE THE UNDERLINED WORD IN EACH VERSE. THEN ON THE OPPOSITE PAGE FIND AND CIRCLE IT IN THE WORD SEARCH PUZZLE.

1 "AND GOD SAID 'LET THERE BE _LIGHTS_ IN THE EXPANSE OF THE SKY TO SEPARATE THE DAY FROM _NIGHT_.'"

                     GENESIS 1:14

2 "GOD MADE TWO GREAT LIGHTS - THE GREATER LIGHT TO GOVERN THE DAY AND THE LESSER LIGHT TO GOVERN THE NIGHT HE ALSO MADE THE _STARS_."

                     GENESIS 1:16

3 "SO GOD CREATED THE GREAT CREATURES OF THE _SEA_ AND EVERY _LIVING_ AND _MOVING_ THING WITH WHICH THE WATER TEAMS ACCORDING TO THEIR KINDS AND EVERY WINGED _BIRD_ ACCORDING TO ITS _KIND_."

                     GENESIS 1:21

6

```
L I G H T
L I K E S E
Y B A E V O
I M N N S C
N E D A U
S T A R S I
L I V I N G
F E Y B J K S W
```
(word search: NIGHT, MOVING, DAY, STARS, LIVING)

7

ZANY CODE BUSTER

USE THE CODE CHART BELOW TO DECODE THE MYSTERY VERSE

(code chart symbols)

CONT'D ON THE NEXT PAGE

8

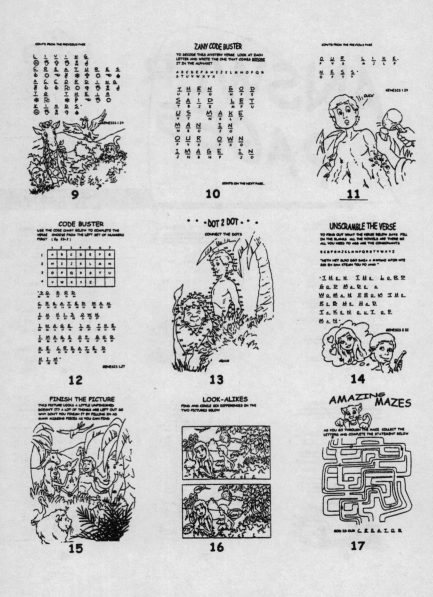

9

GENESIS 1:24

ZANY CODE BUSTER

TO DECODE THIS MYSTERY VERSE, LOOK AT EACH
LETTER AND WRITE THE ONE THAT COMES BEFORE
IT IN THE ALPHABET.

ABCDEFGHIJKLMNOPQR
STUVWXYZ

CONT'D ON THE NEXT PAGE

10

GENESIS 1:29

11

CODE BUSTER

USE THE CODE CHART BELOW TO COMPLETE THE
VERSE. CHOOSE FROM THE LEFT SET OF NUMBERS
FIRST. (Eg 23-1)

GENESIS 1:27

12

• • DOT 2 DOT • •

CONNECT THE DOTS

ADAM

13

UNSCRAMBLE THE VERSE

TO FIND OUT WHAT THE VERSE BELOW SAYS, FILL
IN THE BLANKS. ALL THE VOWELS ARE THERE SO
ALL YOU NEED TO ADD ARE THE CONSONANTS.

GENESIS 2:22

14

FINISH THE PICTURE

THIS PICTURE LOOKS A LITTLE UNFINISHED.
DOESN'T IT? A LOT OF THINGS ARE LEFT OUT SO
WHY DON'T YOU FINISH IT BY FILLING IN AS
MANY MISSING PIECES AS YOU CAN FIND.

15

LOOK-ALIKES

FIND AND CIRCLE SIX DIFFERENCES IN THE
TWO PICTURES BELOW

16

AMAZING MAZES

AS YOU GO THROUGH THE MAZE, COLLECT THE
LETTERS AND COMPLETE THE STATEMENT BELOW

GOD IS OUR C R E A T O R

17

° ° ° SQUARE GAME ° ° °

COLOR IN THE AREAS THAT HAVE A SQUARE TO
COMPLETE THE VERSE BELOW

"GOD SAW ALL THAT HE HAD MADE, AND IT WAS
VERY _ _ _ _."   GENESIS 1:31

18

PICTURE FRAMES
WHAT COULD THE PICTURE BE??

DRAW EXACTLY WHAT IS IN EACH NUMBERED
FRAME AT THE TOP OF THE PAGE INTO EACH FRAME
OF THE SAME NUMBER IN THE GRID BELOW

19

PICTURE FRAMES
WHAT COULD THE PICTURE BE??

DRAW EXACTLY WHAT IS IN EACH NUMBERED
FRAME AT THE TOP OF THE PAGE INTO EACH FRAME
OF THE SAME NUMBER IN THE GRID BELOW

20

TRUE / FALSE

1 THE FIRST THING GOD CREATED WAS THE
   TREES

                    TRUE ____ FALSE _X_

2 GOD SPOKE ALL CREATION INTO EXISTENCE

                    TRUE _X_ FALSE ____

3 MAN CREATED WOMAN

                    TRUE ____ FALSE _X_

4 WE ARE CREATED IN THE IMAGE OF GOD

                    TRUE _X_ FALSE ____

5 GOD NAMED ALL THE ANIMALS

                    TRUE ____ FALSE _X_

21

WORD SEARCH

CROSS OUT EVERY LETTER THAT APPEARS AT
LEAST FOUR TIMES IN THE PUZZLE TO FIND THE
WORD THAT COMPLETES THE SENTENCE

GOD THE ____ ____ ____

22

UNSCRAMBLE THE VERSE

TO FIND OUT WHAT THE VERSE BELOW SAYS, FILL
IN THE BLANKS. ALL THE VOWELS ARE THERE SO
ALL YOU NEED TO ADD ARE THE CONSONANTS

B C D F G H J K L M N P Q R S T V W X Z

"A _A_H_R O_ _H_ _A_H_R_E__ A _RO_EC_OR OF
_W_DOW_ I_ _OD I_ _I_ HOL_ _WE_LI__."

"A F_ _H_R _O _H_
_A_H_RL_ __ A
_IE_DE_ OF _I_OW _
I_ _OD I_ _I_ HOL_
_WELLI__."
                                    PSALM 68:5

23

CODE BUSTER

USE THE CODE CHART BELOW TO COMPLETE THE
VERSE. CHOOSE FROM THE LEFT SET OF NUMBERS
FIRST (Eg 3>2)

	1	2	3	4	5	6	7
1	A	B	C	D	E	F	G
2	H	I	J	K	L	M	N
3	O	P	Q	R	S	T	U
4	V	W	X	Y	Z		

H_ W_LL C_LL OUT
TO M_ YOU AR_ MY
F_TH_R MY GOD
TH_ ROCK MY
S_VIOUR.

24

AMAZING MAZES

ADAM AND EVE ARE PLAYING HIDE AND SEEK. BUT
THE GARDEN IS SO BIG THAT ADAM IS HAVING A
HARD TIME FINDING EVE. CAN YOU HELP HIM
FIND THE WAY?

25

TWICE THE FUN

UNSCRAMBLE THE UNDERLINED WORDS IN THE
VERSE. THEN ON THE OPPOSITE PAGE FIND AND
CIRCLE THEM IN THE WORD SEARCH PUZZLE

"BUT YOU ARE OUR _HEART_, THOUGH ABRAHAM
DOES NOT _KNOW_ US OR _ISRAEL_ ACKNOWLEDGE US
YOU O _LORD_ ARE OUR FATHER OUR _REDEEMER_
_____ KNOW
OUR _____

                                    ISAIAH 63:16

CONT'D ON THE NEXT PANEL

26

27

ZANY CODE BUSTER

TO DECODE THIS MYSTERY VERSE LOOK AT EACH LETTER AND WRITE THE ONE THAT COMES **BEFORE** IT IN THE ALPHABET.

A B C D E F G H I J K L M N O P Q R
S T U V W X Y Z

IN THE SAME WAY,
J O   U I F   T B N F   X B Z

LET YOUR LIGHT
M F U   Z P V S   M J H I U

SHINE BEFORE MEN
T J J O F   C F G P S F   N F O

THAT THEY MAY
U I B U   U I F Z   N B Z

SEE YOUR GOOD
T F F   Z P V S   H P P E

DEEDS AND PRAISE
E F F E T   B O E   Q S B J T F

CONT'D ON THE NEXT PAGE.

28

YOUR FATHER IN
Z P V S   G B U I F S   J O

HEAVEN."
I F B W F O

MATTHEW 5:16

29

ZANY CODE BUSTER

USE THE CODE CHART BELOW TO DECODE THE MYSTERY VERSE.

LOOK AT THE

BIRDS OF THE AIR.

THEY DO NOT SOW

CONT'D ON THE NEXT PAGE.

32

OR REAP OR STORE

AWAY IN BARNS, AND

YET YOUR HEAVENLY

FATHER FEEDS THEM

ARE YOU NOT MUCH

MORE VALUABLE THAN

THEY?"

MATTHEW 6:26

33

WORD SEARCH

FIND AND CIRCLE THE WORDS BELOW IN THE WORD SEARCH PUZZLE. LOOK UP DOWN, FORWARD AND DIAGONALLY TO SOLVE THIS ONE.

FATHER
SON
DAUGHTER
CHILD

HEAVEN
GOD
LOVE
CARE

34

FINISH THE VERSE

TO FIND OUT WHAT THE VERSE BELOW SAYS, FILL IN THE BLANKS. ALL THE CONSONANTS ARE THERE SO ALL YOU NEED TO DO IS ADD THE VOWELS.

VOWELS A E I O U

"I WILL BE A FATHER TO
YOU AND YOU WILL BE
MY SONS AND DAUGHTERS."

2 CORINTHIANS 6:18

35

UNSCRAMBLE AND ANSWER

FIRST, UNSCRAMBLE THE WORDS AND WRITE THEM IN THE SPACE BELOW. THEN ON THE FOLLOWING PAGE, LIST ALL THE CIRCLED LETTERS AND UNSCRAMBLE THEM TO SPELL OUT THE ANSWER TO THE QUESTION.

"ON EON SHA ENSE HTE HTRAFE
NO ONE HAS SEEN THE FATHER

CTEPXE HET EON HWO SI BAFO
EXCEPT THE ONE WHO IS FROM

BGO. NYOL EH SHA ENSE HTE
GOD. ONLY HE HAS SEEN THE

EAHPFT."
FATHER

JOHN 6:46

36

CONT'D ON THE NEXT PAGE.

...CONT'D FROM THE PREVIOUS PAGE

Ⓗ Ⓕ Ⓡ Ⓐ Ⓣ Ⓔ

GOD IS OUR HEAVENLY F A T H E R !

37

FINISH THE VERSE

TO FIND OUT WHAT THE VERSE BELOW SAYS FILL IN THE BLANKS. ALL THE CONSONANTS ARE THERE SO ALL YOU NEED TO DO IS ADD THE VOWELS.

VOWELS A E I O U

"MY FATHER WHO HAS
GIVEN THEM TO ME IS
GREATER THAN ALL NO
ONE CAN SNATCH THEM
OUT OF MY FATHER'S
HAND I AND THE FATHER
ARE ONE"

JOHN 10: 29-30

38

HIDDEN ALPHABET

FIND AND CIRCLE EVERY LETTER OF THE ALPHABET THAT HAS BEEN HIDDEN IN THIS PICTURE

39

CODE BUSTER

USE THE CODE CHART BELOW TO COMPLETE THE VERSE. CHOOSE FROM THE LEFT SET OF NUMBERS FIRST (Eg 13=J)

	1	2	3	4	5	6	7
1	A	B	C	D	E	F	G
2	H	I	J	K	L	M	N
3	O	P	Q	R	S	T	U
4	V	W	X	Y	Z		

"JESUS SAID DO
NOT HOLD ON TO
ME FOR I HAVE
NOT YET RETURNED
TO THE FATHER

CONT'D ON THE NEXT PAGE...

42

...CONT'D FROM THE PREVIOUS PAGE

GO INSTEAD TO MY
BROTHERS AND
TELL THEM I AM
RETURNING TO MY
FATHER AND YOUR
FATHER. TO MY GOD
AND YOUR GOD."

JOHN 20:17

43

WORD SEARCH

HOW MANY TIMES CAN YOU FIND THE WORD FATHER IN THE WORD SEARCH PUZZLE BELOW. LOOK UP DOWN FORWARD AND DIAGONALLY TO SOLVE THIS ONE

44

SQUARE GAME

COLOR IN THE AREAS THAT HAVE A SQUARE TO COMPLETE THE SENTENCE BELOW

GOD IS MY F A T H E R !

45

FILL IN THE BLANKS

WORD LIST	
LOVE	AM
HIM	PLEASED
THIS	HEAVEN
VOICE	SON

"AND A V O I C E FROM H E A V E N
SAID T H I S IS MY S O N WHOM I
L O V E WITH H I M I A M WELL
P L E A S E D"

MATTHEW 3:17

47

FINISH THE VERSE

TO FIND OUT WHAT THE VERSE BELOW SAYS FILL IN THE BLANKS. ALL THE CONSONANTS ARE THERE SO ALL YOU NEED TO DO IS ADD THE VOWELS.

VOWELS A E I O U

"ALL THINGS HAVE BEEN
COMMITTED TO ME BY MY
FATHER NO ONE KNOWS
THE SON EXCEPT THE
FATHER. AND NO ONE
KNOWS THE FATHER

CONT'D ON THE NEXT PAGE...

48

EXCEPT THE SON AND
THOSE TO WHOM THE
SON CHOOSES TO
REVEAL HIM"

MATTHEW 11:27

49

ZANY CODE BUSTER

TO DECODE THIS MYSTERY VERSE, LOOK AT EACH LETTER AND WRITE THE ONE THAT COMES BEFORE IT IN THE ALPHABET

ABCDEFGHIJKLMNOPQR
STUVWXYZ

THEN THOSE IN
UIFO UIPTF JO

THE BOAT
UIF CPBU

WORSHIPED HIM
XPSTIJQFE IJN

SAYING TRULY
TBZJOH USVMZ

YOU ARE THE
ZPV BSF UIF

SON OF GOD"
TPO PG HPE

MATTHEW 14:33

50

TWICE THE FUN

UNSCRAMBLE THE UNDERLINED WORDS IN EACH VERSE, THEN DO THE OPPOSITE PAGE FIND AND CIRCLE THEM IN THE WORD SEARCH PUZZLE.

1. "SIMON PETER ANSWERED, 'YOU ARE THE _____, THE SON OF THE LIVING _____.'"

MATTHEW 16:16

CHRIST SON GOD

2. "A _____ CAME FROM THE CLOUD, SAYING, 'THIS IS MY SON WHOM I HAVE CHOSEN; _____ TO HIM.'"

LUKE 9:35

WRITE CLOUD
LISTEN HIM

CONT'D ON THE NEXT PAGE...

52

53

WORD JUMBLE

FILL IN THE BLANK SPACES BY WRITING IN THE OPPOSITE OF EACH WORD BELOW, ANSWERING EACH CLUE CORRECTLY USING THE LETTERS IN THE CIRCLES. COMPLETE THE SENTENCE BELOW.

MOTHER	F A T H E R
DAUGHTER	S O N
DARK	L I G H T
END	B E G I N N I N G
NIGHT	D A Y
MAN	W O M A N

"THE FATHER AND THE SON ARE BOTH ____."

G O D

54

WORD SEARCH

HOW MANY TIMES CAN YOU FIND THE WORD SON BELOW IN THE WORD SEARCH PUZZLE. LOOK UP DOWN, FORWARD AND DIAGONALLY TO SOLVE THIS ONE!

55

UNSCRAMBLE AND ANSWER

FIRST UNSCRAMBLE THE WORDS AND WRITE THEM IN THE SPACES UNDER EACH WORD THEN LIST ALL THE CIRCLED LETTERS BELOW AND UNSCRAMBLE THEM TO SPELL OUT THE ANSWER TO THE QUESTION

"OFR DGO OS VEOLD ETH
FOR GOD SO LOVED THE

LRWBO ANTT EH EGVA IHS
WORLD THAT HE GAVE HIS

NEO DAN LOYN NSO"
ONE AND ONLY SON"

JOHN 3:16

WHO IS JESUS CHRIST?

GODS SON

56

AMAZING MAZES

AS YOU GO THROUGH THE MAZE, COLLECT THE LETTERS AND COMPLETE THE STATEMENT BELOW

GOD LOVES ME

57

FINISH THE VERSE

TO FIND OUT WHAT THE VERSE BELOW SAYS FILL IN THE BLANKS ALL THE CONSONANTS ARE THERE SO ALL YOU NEED TO DO IS ADD THE VOWELS

VOWELS A E I O U

"FATHER THE TIME HAS
COME GLORIFY YOUR
SON THAT YOUR SON
MAY GLORIFY YOU"

JOHN 17:1

58

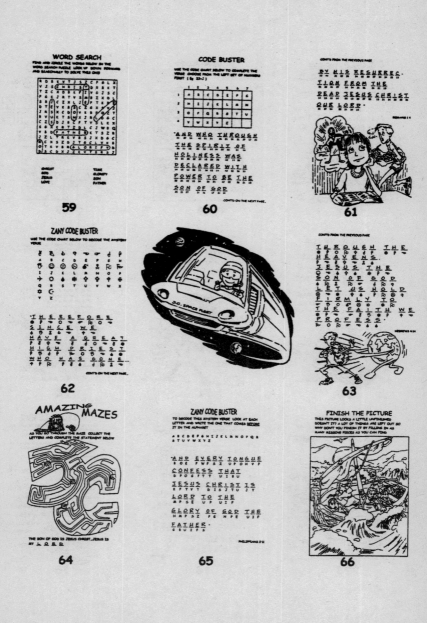

WORD SEARCH
Find and circle the words below in the word search puzzle. Look up, down, forward and diagonally to solve this one.

59

CHRIST
GOD
JESUS
LOVE

TIME
GLORIFY
SON
FATHER

CODE BUSTER
Use the code chart below to complete the verse. Choose from the left set of numbers first (& 23-2)

AND WHO THROUGH
THE SPIRIT OF
HOLINESS WAS
DECLARED WITH
POWER TO BE THE
SON OF GOD

CONT'D ON THE NEXT PAGE.

60

CONT'D FROM THE PREVIOUS PAGE

BY HIS RESURREC-
TION FROM THE
DEAD JESUS CHRIST
OUR LORD.

ROMANS 1:4

61

ZANY CODE BUSTER
Use the code chart below to decode the mystery verse.

THEREFORE
SINCE WE
HAVE A GREAT
HIGH PRIEST
WHO HAS GONE

CONT'D ON THE NEXT PAGE.

62

CONT'D FROM THE PREVIOUS PAGE

THROUGH THE
HEAVENS,
JESUS THE
SON OF GOD
LET US HOLD
FIRMLY
TO THE FAITH WE
PROFESS.

HEBREWS 4:14

63

AMAZING MAZES
As you go through the maze collect the letters and complete the statement below.

THE SON OF GOD IS JESUS CHRIST...JESUS IS
MY L O R D

64

ZANY CODE BUSTER
To decode this mystery verse look at each letter and write the one that comes before it in the alphabet.

ABCDEFGHIJKLMNOPQR
STUVWXYZ

AND EVERY TONGUE
BOE FWFSZ UPOHVF

CONFESS THAT
DPOGFTT UIBU

JESUS CHRIST IS
KFTVT DISJTU JT

LORD TO THE
MPSE UP UIF

GLORY OF GOD THE
HMPSZ PG HPE UIF

FATHER
GBUIFS

PHILIPPIANS 2:11

65

FINISH THE PICTURE
This picture looks a little unfinished doesn't it? A lot of things are left out so why don't you finish it by filling in as many missing pieces as you can find.

66

UNSCRAMBLE THE VERSE

TO FIND OUT WHAT THE VERSE BELOW SAYS FILL IN THE BLANKS. ALL THE VOWELS ARE THERE SO ALL YOU NEED TO ADD ARE THE CONSONANTS

"_S _O_T _TZ_ _ _W _ZE_W_ _EZ_ _ZW_ _ _LZ_ T_C_N_N_ _T _L_ N_ _N_ "

"_O _H_N _V__ _Z _OV _E_E_V_D _Z_V_ _H_I_T _Z _O_D _O__I__E _O _I_E I_ _I_."

COLOSSIANS 2:6

67

LOOK-ALIKES

FIND AND CIRCLE EIGHT DIFFERENCES IN THE TWO PICTURES BELOW

68

PICTURE FRAMES

WHAT COULD THE PICTURE BE?

DRAW EXACTLY WHAT IS IN EACH NUMBERED FRAME AT THE TOP OF THE PAGE INTO EACH FRAME OF THE SAME NUMBER IN THE GRID BELOW

69

UNSCRAMBLE THE VERSE

TO FIND OUT WHAT THE VERSE BELOW SAYS FILL IN THE BLANKS. ALL THE VOWELS ARE THERE SO ALL YOU NEED TO ADD ARE THE CONSONANTS

"NEITHER HEIGHT NOR DEPTH NOR ANYTHING ELSE IN ALL CREATION WILL BE ABLE TO SEPARATE US FROM"

CONT'D ON THE NEXT PAGE.

70

CONT'D FROM THE PREVIOUS PAGE

THE LOVE OF GOD THAT IS IN CHRIST JESUS OUR LORD

ROMANS 8:39

71

WORD SEARCH

CROSS OUT EVERY LETTER THAT APPEARS FOUR TIMES IN THE PUZZLE TO FIND THE WORD THAT COMPLETES THE SENTENCE

JESUS IS L O R D OF ALL!

72

HIDDEN ALPHABET

FIND AND CIRCLE EVERY LETTER OF THE ALPHABET THAT HAS BEEN HIDDEN IN THIS PICTURE.

73

CODE BUSTER

USE THE CODE CHART BELOW TO COMPLETE THE VERSE. CHOOSE FROM THE LEFT SET OF NUMBERS FIRST (Eg. 23=J)

	1	2	3	4	5	6	7
1	A	B	C	D	E	F	G
2	H	I	J	K	L	M	N
3	O	P	Q	R	S	T	U
4	V	W	X	Y	Z		

"AND WE HAVE SEEN AND TESTIFY THAT THE FATHER HAS SENT HIS SON TO BE SAVIOUR OF THE WORLD."

1 JOHN 4:14

74

UNSCRAMBLE THE VERSE

TO FIND OUT WHAT THE VERSE BELOW SAYS FILL IN THE BLANKS. ALL THE VOWELS ARE THERE SO ALL YOU NEED TO ADD ARE THE CONSONANTS

"YOU ARE ALL SONS OF GOD THROUGH FAITH IN CHRIST JESUS, FOR ALL OF YOU WHO WERE BAPTIZED INTO CHRIST HAVE CLOTHED YOURSELVES WITH CHRIST."

GALATIANS 3:26-27

75

HIDDEN: ALPHABET

FIND AND CIRCLE EVERY LETTER OF THE ALPHABET THAT HAS BEEN HIDDEN IN THIS PICTURE. THEN USING THOSE LETTERS, COMPLETE THE STATEMENT BELOW.

I AM GOD'S C H I L D

78

FINISH THE VERSE

TO FIND OUT WHAT THE VERSE BELOW SAYS, FILL IN THE BLANKS. ALL THE CONSONANTS ARE THERE SO ALL YOU NEED TO DO IS ADD THE VOWELS.

VOWELS A E I O U

"NOW THE EARTH WAS
FORMLESS AND EMPTY,
DARKNESS WAS OVER
THE SURFACE OF THE
DEEP AND THE SPIRIT
OF GOD WAS HOVERING
OVER THE WATERS"

GENESIS 1.2

80

TWICE THE FUN

UNSCRAMBLE THE UNDERLINED WORDS IN EACH VERSE. THEN ON THE NEXT PAGE, FIND AND CIRCLE THEM IN THE WORD SEARCH PUZZLE.

1 "WHERE CAN I GO FROM YOUR _____?
   "WHERE CAN I FLEE FROM YOUR _____?"
   PSALMS 139.7

   S P I R I T   P R E S E N C E

2 "I WILL POUR OUT MY SPIRIT ON YOUR _____"
   ISAIAH 44.3

   P O U R   O F F S P R I N G

3 "AND I HAVE FILLED HER WITH THE SPIRIT OF GOD"
   EXODUS 31.3

   F I L L E D   G O D

CONT'D ON THE NEXT PAGE.

81

...CONT'D FROM THE PREVIOUS PAGE

82

CODE BUSTER

USE THE CODE CHART BELOW TO COMPLETE THE VERSE. CHOOSE FROM THE LEFT SET OF NUMBERS FIRST. (Eg 22=T)

	1	2	3	4	5	6	7
1	A	B	C	D	E	F	G
2	H	I	J	K	L	M	N
3	O	P	Q	R	S	T	U
4	V	W	X	Y	Z		

"I BAPTIZE YOU
WITH WATER FOR
REPENTANCE BUT
AFTER ME WILL
COME ONE WHO IS

CONT'D ON THE NEXT PAGE.

83

CONT'D FROM PREVIOUS PAGE

MORE POWERFUL

THAN I WHOSE

SANDALS I AM NOT

FIT TO CARRY HE

WILL BAPTIZE YOU

WITH THE HOLY

SPIRIT AND FIRE"

MATTHEW 3.11

WHOAA!

84

UNSCRAMBLE THE VERSE

TO FIND OUT WHAT THE VERSE BELOW SAYS, FILL IN THE BLANKS. ALL THE VOWELS ARE THERE SO ALL YOU NEED TO ADD ARE THE CONSONANTS.

"F YOU THEN THOUGH YOU ARE EVIL KNOW HOW TO GIVE GOOD GIFTS TO YOUR CHILDREN HOW MUCH MORE WILL YOUR FATHER IN HEAVEN GIVE THE HOLY SPIRIT TO THOSE WHO ASK HIM"

IF YOU THEN THOUGH
YOU ARE EVIL KNOW
HOW TO GIVE GOOD
GIFTS TO YOUR
CHILDREN HOW MUCH
MORE WILL YOUR
FATHER IN HEAVEN
GIVE THE HOLY SPIRIT
TO THOSE WHO ASK HIM"

LUKE 11.13

85

AMAZING MAZES

THE HOLY SPIRIT WANTS TO COME TO YOU. GO THROUGH THE MAZE TO FIND THE PATH HE TAKES.

86

FILL IN THE BLANKS

WORD LIST

COUNSELOR	REMIND
EVERYTHING	HOLY SPIRIT
NAME	FATHER
TEACH	THINGS

BUT THE C O U N S E L O R THE H O L Y S P I R I T WHOM THE F A T H E R WILL SEND IN MY N A M E WILL T E A C H YOU ALL T H I N G S AND WILL R E M I N D YOU OF E V E R Y T H I N G I HAVE SAID TO YOU"

JOHN 14.26

87

°°° SQUARE GAME °°°

COLOR IN THE AREAS THAT HAVE A SQUARE TO
FIND THE ANSWER TO COMPLETE THE VERSE BELOW

"BUT WHEN HE THE S P I R I T OF
TRUTH COMES HE WILL GUIDE YOU INTO ALL
TRUTH " JOHN 16:13

88

LOOK-ALIKES

FIND AND CIRCLE TEN DIFFERENCES IN THE
TWO PICTURES BELOW

89

ZANY CODE BUSTER

USE THE CODE CHART BELOW TO DECODE THE
MYSTERY VERSE

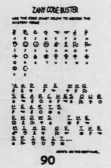

...CONT'D ON THE NEXT PAGE.

90

...CONT'D FROM THE PREVIOUS PAGE

ROMANS 8:27

91

FINISH THE PICTURE

THIS PICTURE LOOKS A LITTLE UNFINISHED
DOESN'T IT? A LOT OF THINGS ARE LEFT OUT SO
WHY DON'T YOU FINISH IT BY FILLING IN AS
MANY MISSING PIECES AS YOU CAN FIND

92

AMAZING MAZES

AS YOU GO THROUGH THE MAZE, COLLECT THE
LETTERS AND COMPLETE THE VERSE BELOW

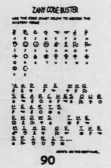

"BUT GOD HAS REVEALED IT TO US BY HIS
S P I R I T THE SPIRIT SEARCHES ALL
THINGS, EVEN THE DEEP THINGS OF GOD."
1 CORINTHIANS 2:10

93

CODE BUSTER

USE THE CODE CHART BELOW TO COMPLETE THE
VERSE CHOOSE FROM THE LEFT SET OF NUMBERS
FIRST (Ex: 13=J)

	1	2	3	4	5	6
1	A	B	C	D	E	F
2	G	H	I	J	K	L
3	M	N	O	P	Q	R
4	S	T	U	V	W	X
5	Y	Z				

WE HAVE NOT

RECEIVED THE

SPIRIT OF THE

WORLD BUT THE

SPIRIT WHO IS-

CONT'D ON THE NEXT PAGE.

94

...CONT'D FROM THE PREVIOUS PAGE

FROM GOD THAT WE

MAY UNDERSTAND

WHAT GOD HAS

FREELY GIVEN

US.

1 CORINTHIANS 2:12

GO AWAY!
I'VE TOLD YOU
BEFORE... I ALREADY
HAVE THE ONLY SPIRIT
I'LL EVER NEED!

95

FILL IN THE BLANKS

WORD LIST

RECEIVED — TEMPLE
KNOW — HOLY SPIRIT
YOU — GOD
BODY — YOUR

"DO YOU NOT **K N O W** THAT **Y O U R**

B O D Y IS A **T E M P L E** OF THE

H O L Y S P I R I T WHO IS IN

Y O U WHOM YOU HAVE

R E C E I V E D FROM **G O D** "

96

UNSCRAMBLE AND ANSWER

FIRST UNSCRAMBLE THE WORDS AND WRITE THEM IN THE SPACES UNDER EACH WORD. THEN LIST ALL THE CIRCLED LETTERS BELOW AND UNSCRAMBLE THEM TO SPELL OUT THE ANSWER TO THE QUESTION

"EH DAENTONI SU TSE
(H)E ANOINTED US SET

SHI LSEA FO POIWHNSER
HIS SEAL OF OWNE(R)SHIP

NO SU DAN TPU SHI TPSIIR
ON US (A)ND PUT HIS SPIRIT

NI RUO SHTERA SA A
IN OUR HEARTS AS A

CONT'D ON THE NEXT PAGE

97

...CONT'D FROM PREVIOUS PAGE

.TDEESFO SSNVIJAEREATH
DEPOSIT GUARAN(T)EEING

TWAN BI OT ECHO
WHAT IS TO COME(E)

2 CORINTHIANS 1:22

WHERE DOES THE HOLY SPIRIT LIVE?

IN MY (H)(E)(A)(R)(T)

98

PICTURE FRAMES
WHAT COULD THE PICTURE BE?

DRAW EXACTLY WHAT IS IN EACH NUMBERED FRAME AT THE TOP OF THE PAGE INTO EACH FRAME OF THE SAME NUMBER IN THE GRID BELOW

99

ZANY CODE BUSTER
USE THE CODE CHART BELOW TO DECODE THE MYSTERY VERSE

CONT'D ON THE NEXT PAGE

100

...CONT'D FROM THE PREVIOUS PAGE

GALATIANS 3:2

I CAN HAVE THEM ALL??

101

WORD SEARCH
HOW MANY TIMES CAN YOU FIND THE WORD HOLY SPIRIT BELOW IN THE WORD SEARCH PUZZLE. LOOK UP DOWN FORWARDS BACKWARDS AND DIAGONALLY TO SOLVE THIS ONE

102

• • DOT 2 DOT • •
CONNECT THE DOTS

106

HIDDEN ALPHABET
FIND AND CIRCLE EVERY LETTER OF THE ALPHABET THAT HAS BEEN HIDDEN IN THIS PICTURE AND FINISH THE SENTENCE BELOW

THE HOLY SPIRIT IS MY **T E A C H E R**

107

MULTIPLE CHOICE

CIRCLE THE CORRECT ANSWER

1. "IN THE BEGINNING GOD CREATED THE..."
   - A SEA
   - B HEAVENS AND EARTH
   - C APPLE TREE

2. GOD MADE MAN IN THE IMAGE OF...
   - A MONKEYS
   - B MAN
   - C GOD

3. GOD CREATED EVE OUT OF ADAM'S...
   - A RIB
   - B ARM
   - C TOE

CONT'D ON THE NEXT PAGE.

108

CONT'D FROM THE PREVIOUS PAGE

4. WE ARE CHILDREN OF...
   - A GOD
   - B ADAM
   - C OUR PARENTS

5. WHEN JESUS CALLED GOD, "ABBA" HE WAS SAYING...
   - A FATHER
   - B CREATOR
   - C LORD

6. WE BELIEVE IN...
   - A ONE GOD
   - B THREE GODS
   - C ONE GOD IN THREE PERSONS

YES!! IT'S ALL SO CLEAR NOW! WELL, KINDA...MAYBE THREE PARTS... BUT ALL ONE EGG!!

109

TRUE / FALSE

1. A VOICE CAME FROM HEAVEN AND SAID "THIS IS JESUS"

   TRUE ___ FALSE X

2. GOD CREATED EVE

   TRUE ✓ FALSE ___

3. JESUS CHRIST IS THE SON OF GOD.

   TRUE ✓ FALSE ___

4. JESUS USED HIS GODLY POWERS DURING HIS MINISTRY

   TRUE ✓ FALSE ___

5. JESUS IS SAVIOUR OF THE WORLD

   TRUE ✓ FALSE ___

110

TRUE / FALSE

1. WE BECOME CHILDREN OF GOD BY GOING TO CHURCH

   TRUE ___ FALSE X

2. THE HOLY SPIRIT WAS WITH GOD WHEN HE CREATED THE HEAVENS AND THE EARTH

   TRUE ✓ FALSE ___

3. GOD THE FATHER WILL GIVE YOU THE HOLY SPIRIT IF YOU ASK

   TRUE ✓ FALSE ___

4. THE HOLY SPIRIT DOESN'T KNOW MY MIND AND HEART

   TRUE ___ FALSE X

5. THE HOLY SPIRIT IS GOD.

   TRUE ✓ FALSE ___

111

TWICE THE FUN

UNSCRAMBLE THE UNDERLINED WORDS IN THE VERSE BELOW. THEN, ON THE NEXT PAGE, FIND AND CIRCLE THEM IN THE WORD SEARCH PUZZLE

"YOURS O LORD IS THE GREATNESS AND THE REWOP AND THE YLORG AND THE MAJESTY AND THE ROLSPENDOR FOR EVERYTHING IN VENHEA AND THERA IS YOURS. YOURS, O LORD, IS THE MINGDKO. YOU ARE EXALTED AS DAHE OVER ALL. WEALTH AND HONOR COME FROM UYO. YOU ARE THE RELUR OF ALL GSNITH. IN YOUR HANDS ARE STRENGTH AND POWER TO EXALT AND EVIG STRENGTH TO ALL."

POWER   GLORY

HEAVEN   EARTH

YOURS   KINGDOM

HEAD   YOU   RULER

THINGS   GIVE

1 CHRONICLES 29:11-12

GOD IS KING OF THE UNIVERSE.

CONT'D ON THE NEXT PAGE.

113

CONT'D FROM THE PREVIOUS PAGE.

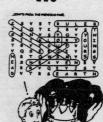

114

AMAZING MAZES

SOMETIMES LIFE CAN SEEM LIKE A MAZE AND IT IS HARD TO FIND THE WAY. IT IS GOOD TO KNOW THAT WE ARE ALWAYS IN GOD'S HAND AND HE KNOWS THE WAY WE SHOULD GO

ALL THINGS ARE IN HIS HAND
HE IS IN CONTROL OF MY LIFE.

115

CODE BUSTER

USE THE CODE CHART BELOW TO COMPLETE THE VERSE. CHOOSE FROM THE LEFT SET OF NUMBERS FIRST (Eg 23=J)

	1	2	3	4	5	6	7
1	A	B	C	D	E	F	G
2	H	I	J	K	L	M	N
3	O	P	Q	R	S	T	U
4	V	W	X	Y	Z		

RIGHTEOUS ARE

YOU O LORD AND

YOUR LAWS ARE

RIGHT

PSALM 119:137

GOD IS RIGHTEOUS.
HE CANNOT SIN AGAINST ME

116

ZANY CODE BUSTER

TO DECODE THIS MYSTERY VERSE LOOK AT EACH LETTER AND WRITE THE ONE THAT COMES BEFORE IT IN THE ALPHABET.

A B C D E F G H I J K L M N O P Q R
S T U V W X Y Z

HE IS THE ROCK
IF JT UIF SPDL

HIS WORKS ARE
IJT XPSLT BSF

PERFECT AND ALL
QFSGFDU BOE BMM

HIS WAYS ARE JUST A
IJT XBZT BSF KVTUB

FAITHFUL GOD
GBJUIGVM HPE

WHO DOES NO...
XIP EPFT OP

GOD IS JUST.

CONT'D ON THE NEXT PAGE.

117

CONT'D FROM THE PREVIOUS PAGE

WRONG UPRIGHT
AND JUST IS HE

IT'S JUST NOT FAIR!

DEUTERONOMY 32:4

DID IT EVER
OCCUR TO YOU THAT
IF ONE—STOPPED...?

HE WILL ALWAYS BE FAIR WITH ME.

118

ZANY CODE BUSTER

USE THE CODE CHART BELOW TO DECODE THE MYSTERY VERSE

WHOEVER

DOES NOT

LOVE DOES

NOT KNOW...

GOD IS LOVE
CONT'D ON THE NEXT PAGE.

119

CONT'D FROM THE PREVIOUS PAGE

GOD BECAUSE
GOD IS LOVE.

1 JOHN 4:8

HE WANTS TO HELP ME GET THE MOST OUT OF LIFE.

120

UNSCRAMBLE AND ANSWER

FIRST UNSCRAMBLE THE WORDS AND WRITE THEM IN THE SPACES UNDER EACH WORD. THEN LIST ALL THE CIRCLED LETTERS BELOW AND UNSCRAMBLE THEM TO COMPLETE THE STATEMENT

EHT LEATNER DGO SI
THE ETERNAL GOD IS

RYOU EFEGRFU ADN
YOUR REFUGE AND

HUTNADEENR ERA
UNDERNEATH ARE

HET GENEIBVTLSA SARM
THE EVERLASTING ARMS

DEUTERONOMY 33:27

GOD IS ETERNAL

THE PLAN HE IS WORKING OUT FOR ME IS EVERLASTING

121

FINISH THE VERSE

TO FIND OUT WHAT THE VERSE BELOW SAYS FILL IN THE BLANKS. ALL THE CONSONANTS ARE THERE SO ALL YOU NEED TO DO IS ADD THE VOWELS

VOWELS A E I O U

"O LORD YOU HAVE
SEARCHED ME AND YOU
KNOW ME YOU KNOW WHEN I
SIT AND WHEN I RISE YOU
PERCEIVE MY THOUGHTS FROM
AFAR YOU DISCERN MY GOING
OUT AND MY LYING DOWN.
YOU ARE FAMILIAR WITH
ALL MY WAYS BEFORE A WORD
IS ON MY TONGUE.

GOD IS ALL KNOWING

122

CONT'D FROM THE PREVIOUS PAGE

YOU KNOW IT COMPLETELY
O LORD YOU HEM ME IN—
BEHIND AND BEFORE YOU
HAVE LAID YOUR HAND UPON
ME"

HE KNOWS ALL ABOUT ME AND MY SITUATION AND HOW TO WORK IT OUT FOR GOOD

123

HIDDEN ALPHABET

FIND AND CIRCLE EVERY LETTER OF THE ALPHABET THAT HAS BEEN HIDDEN IN THIS PICTURE AND FINISH THE SENTENCE BELOW

GOD KNOWS THE WAY
I SHOULD GO

124

UNSCRAMBLE THE VERSE

TO FIND OUT WHAT THE VERSE BELOW SAYS FILL IN THE BLANKS. ALL THE VOWELS ARE THERE SO ALL YOU NEED TO ADD ARE THE CONSONANTS

WHERE CAN I GO FROM
YOUR SPIRIT? WHERE
CAN I FLEE FROM YOUR
PRESENCE? IF I GO UP
TO THE HEAVENS YOU
ARE THERE IF I MAKE
MY BED IN THE DEPTHS
YOU ARE THERE

CONT'D ON THE NEXT PAGE.

127

CONT'D FROM THE PREVIOUS PAGE

(128)

"...IF I RISE ON THE
WINGS OF THE DAWN
IF I SETTLE ON THE
FAR SIDE OF THE SEA
EVEN THERE YOUR HAND
WILL GUIDE ME YOUR
RIGHT HAND WILL HOLD
ME FAST."

PSALMS 139:7-10

GOD IS EVERYWHERE.
THERE IS NO PLACE I CAN GO THAT HE
WILL NOT TAKE CARE OF ME.

128

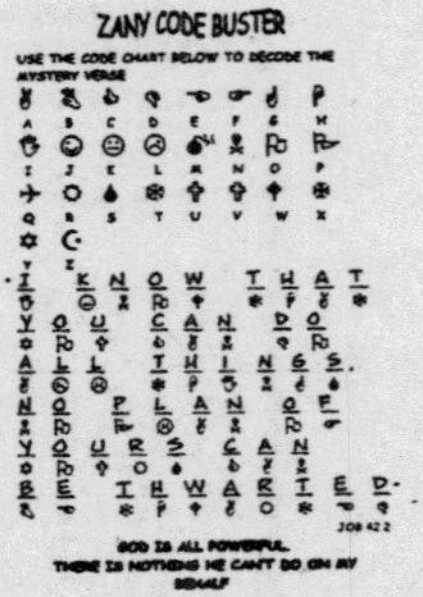

ZANY CODE BUSTER

USE THE CODE CHART BELOW TO DECODE THE
MYSTERY VERSE

"KNOW THAT
FOR I AM
GOD AND
OF ALL THINGS
THERE IS
NOTHING I
PLAN AND
YOURS IN
THE WATER..."

JOB 42:2

GOD IS ALL POWERFUL.
THERE IS NOTHING HE CAN'T DO ON MY
BEHALF

129

TWICE THE FUN

UNSCRAMBLE THE UNDERLINED WORDS IN THE
VERSE BELOW THEN ON THE NEXT PAGE FIND
AND CIRCLE THEM IN THE WORD SEARCH PUZZLE

"INTO YOUR HANDS I COMMIT MY SPIRIT
REDEEM ME O LORD THE GOD OF TRUTH."

HANDS COMMIT

SPIRIT REDEEM

LORD TRUTH

PSALMS 31:5

CONT'D ON THE NEXT PAGE.

130

CONT'D FROM THE PREVIOUS PAGE

GOD IS TRUTH
GOD CAN NOT LIE TO ME

131

AMAZING MAZES

AS YOU GO THROUGH THE MAZE, COLLECT THE
LETTERS AND COMPLETE THE VERSE BELOW

"I THE LORD DO NOT C H A N G E."
MALACHI 3:6

GOD IS UNCHANGING

132

SQUARE GAME

COLOR IN THE AREAS THAT HAVE A SQUARE TO
COMPLETE THE STATEMENT BELOW

I CAN DEPEND ON H I M!

133

FILL IN THE BLANKS

WORD LIST

FEAR	HOLY
GLORY	WORSHIP
NAME	RIGHTEOUS

"WHO WILL NOT F E A R YOU O LORD

AND BRING G L O R Y TO YOUR N A M E?

FOR YOU ALONE ARE H O L Y ALL

NATIONS WILL COME AND

W O R S H I P BEFORE YOU FOR YOUR

R I G H T E O U S ACTS HAVE BEEN

REVEALED."

REVELATION 15:4

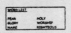

134

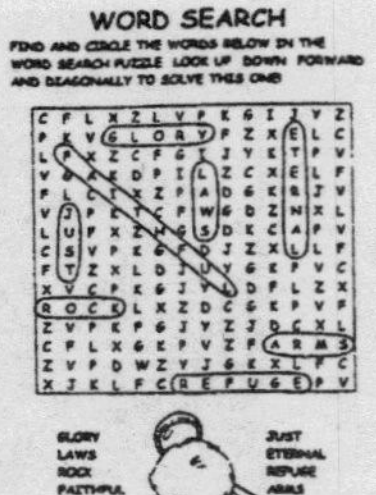

WORD SEARCH

FIND AND CIRCLE THE WORDS BELOW IN THE
WORD SEARCH PUZZLE. LOOK UP DOWN FORWARD
AND DIAGONALLY TO SOLVE THIS ONE!

GLORY
LAWS
ROCK
FAITHFUL

JUST
ETERNAL
REFUGE
ARMS

135

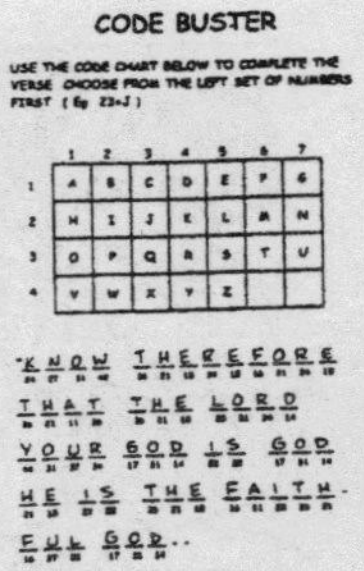

CODE BUSTER

USE THE CODE CHART BELOW TO COMPLETE THE
VERSE. CHOOSE FROM THE LEFT SET OF NUMBERS
FIRST (Eg 23=J)

	1	2	3	4	5	6	7
1	A	B	C	D	E	F	G
2	H	I	J	K	L	M	N
3	O	P	Q	R	S	T	U
4	V	W	X	Y	Z		

"KNOW THEREFORE

THAT THE LORD

YOUR GOD IS GOD

HE IS THE FAITH

FUL GOD..."

136

CONT'D FROM THE PREVIOUS PAGE

KEEPING HIS COVENANT OF LOVE TO A THOUSAND GENERATIONS OF THOSE WHO LOVE HIM AND KEEP HIS COMMANDS.

DEUTERONOMY 7:9

GOD IS HOLY,
HE WILL BE HOLY IN ALL HE DOES

137

• • DOT 2 DOT • •
CONNECT THE DOTS

WHEN YOU PRAY, YOU CAN ALWAYS COUNT ON GOD'S CHARACTER

138

UNSCRAMBLE AND ANSWER

FIRST, UNSCRAMBLE THE WORDS AND WRITE THEM IN THE SPACES UNDER EACH WORD. THEN LIST ALL THE CIRCLED LETTERS BELOW AND UNSCRAMBLE THEM TO COMPLETE THE STATEMENT

"REETFOEH CINSE EW EHVA
THEREFORE SINCE WE HAVE

EBNE TFIDEJISU GRUNTOH
BEEN JUSTIFIED THROUGH

THFIA EW EVHA CPEAE TIWH
FAITH WE HAVE PEACE WITH

DOG UTGHORH URO ROLD
GOD THROUGH OUR LORD

SUEJS RCITHS"
JESUS CHRIST

ROMANS 5:1

I HAVE P E A C E WITH GOD

142

FILL IN THE BLANKS

WORD LIST	
BLAMELESS	SIGHT
WORLD	CREATION
HOLY	CHOSE

FOR HE CHOSE US IN HIM BEFORE THE CREATION OF THE WORLD TO BE HOLY AND BLAMELESS IN HIS SIGHT.

EPHESIANS 1:4

I AM ACCEPTED BY GOD!

143

UNSCRAMBLE THE VERSE

TO FIND OUT WHAT THE VERSE BELOW SAYS, FILL IN THE BLANKS. ALL THE VOWELS ARE THERE SO ALL YOU NEED TO ADD ARE THE CONSONANTS.

"ETY OT LAL OHW EEVRECE ANG OT BEMTO HOW LVEBEIE NE SHE RANN, EH EVGA HET HGTIG OT OEABOX KIEMHLD FO OGD

"YET TO ALL WHO RECEIVE HIM TO THOSE WHO BELIEVE IN HIS NAME HE GAVE THE RIGHT TO BECOME CHILDREN OF GOD

JOHN 1:12

CHILD, SILLY! NOT BABY

144

WORD SEARCH

FIND AND CIRCLE THE WORDS BELOW IN THE WORD SEARCH PUZZLE. LOOK UP, DOWN, FORWARD AND DIAGONALLY TO SOLVE THIS ONE!

PEACE
FAITH
RECEIVE
HOLY
ETERNAL

145

LOOK-ALIKES

FIND AND CIRCLE TWELVE DIFFERENCES IN THE TWO PICTURES BELOW

146

FINISH THE VERSE

TO FIND OUT WHAT THE VERSE BELOW SAYS FILL IN THE BLANKS. ALL THE CONSONANTS ARE THERE SO ALL YOU NEED TO DO IS ADD THE VOWELS.

VOWELS A E I O U

"DON'T YOU KNOW THAT YOU YOURSELVES ARE GOD'S TEMPLE AND THAT GOD'S SPIRIT LIVES IN YOU?

1 CORINTHIANS 3:16

I HAVE THE HOLY SPIRIT INSIDE ME!

147

ZANY CODE BUSTER

USE THE CODE CHART BELOW TO DECODE THE MYSTERY VERSE

CONT'D ON THE NEXT PAGE

148

CONT'D FROM THE PREVIOUS PAGE

149

Word search grid

```
W H O   G I V E S
G E N E R O U S L Y
T O   A L L   W I T H
O U T   F I N D
I N G   F A U L T
A N D   I T   W I L L
B E   G I V E N
H I M
```

THAT DIDN'T FEEL TOO GOOD...

MAYBE YOU SHOULD TRY THIS?? JAMES 1:5

I HAVE ACCESS TO GOD'S WISDOM!

TWICE THE FUN

UNSCRAMBLE THE UNDERLINED WORDS IN THE VERSE BELOW THEN ON THE NEXT PAGE FIND AND CIRCLE THEM IN THE WORD SEARCH PUZZLE

"LET US THEN APPROACH THE ORNETH OF GRACE WITH CONFIDENCE SO THAT WE MAY RECEIVE YRMEC AND FIND EEGAC TO HELP US IN OUR TIME OF EEDN."

T H R O N E   M E R C Y

G R A C E   N E E D

HEBREWS 4:16

I AM HELPED BY GOD!

150

CONT'D ON THE NEXT PAGE

CONT'D FROM THE PREVIOUS PAGE

```
S Q D W G L Z M
K T H R O N E W
F R N P Y C A M
A L H E A R F E
P X O R D J N R
R N G E F Q V C
I F F S N R D Y
N E E D R F P J
```

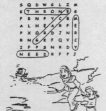

151

HIDDEN ALPHABET

FIND AND CIRCLE EVERY LETTER OF THE ALPHABET THAT HAS BEEN HIDDEN IN THIS PICTURE AND FINISH THE SENTENCE BELOW

I RECEIVE M E R C Y BECAUSE OF GOD'S GRACE

152

AMAZING MAZES

FIND THE WAY TO THE THRONE OF GRACE

153

CODE BUSTER

USE THE CODE CHART BELOW TO COMPLETE THE VERSE. CHOOSE FROM THE LEFT SET OF NUMBERS FIRST (Eg 23=2)

	1	2	3	4	5	6	7
1	A	B	C	D	E	F	G
2	H	I	J	K	L	M	N
3	O	P	Q	R	S	T	U
4	V	W	X	Y	Z		

N O T   O N L Y   I S   T H I S

S O   B U T   W E   A L S O

R E J O I C E   I N   G O D

T H R O U G H   O U R   L O R D

J E S U S   C H R I S T

154

CONT'D ON THE NEXT PAGE

CONT'D FROM THE PREVIOUS PAGE

T H R O U G H   W H O M

W E   H A V E   N O W

R E C E I V E D

R E C O N C I L I A T I O N ·

ROMANS 5:11

HEY- WHAT IN THE WORLD DOES REC RECO RECON- WHATEVER MEAN.

"RECONCILE" IT MEANS TO BE MADE "FRIENDS WITH AGAIN"... SO WE'RE MADE FRIENDS AGAIN WITH GOD!

COOL!

I AM RECONCILED TO GOD!

155

ZANY CODE BUSTER

TO DECODE THIS MYSTERY VERSE, LOOK AT EACH LETTER AND WRITE THE ONE THAT COMES BEFORE IT IN THE ALPHABET

A B C D E F G H I J K L M N O P Q R S T U V W X Y Z

T H E R E F O R E   T H E R E

I S   N O W   N O   C O N D E M

N A T I O N   F O R   T H O S E

W H O

?!

CONT'D ON THE NEXT PAGE

156

CONT'D FROM THE PREVIOUS PAGE

ARE IN CHRIST
YES? SO DISJTU

JESUS.
E F T V T

WHAT ABOUT CON-
DEM-NA-TION? WHAT DOES
"THAT MEAN"?

TO BE
CONVICTED
AS GUILTY. TO BE JUDGED
TO BE BLAMED, CRITICIZED,
DOOMED SEN

ROMANS 8:1

THERE IS NO CONDEMNATION FOR ME!

157

PICTURE FRAMES
WHAT COULD THE PICTURE BE???

DRAW EXACTLY WHAT IS IN EACH NUMBERED
FRAME AT THE TOP OF THE PAGE INTO EACH FRAME
OF THE SAME NUMBER IN THE GRID BELOW

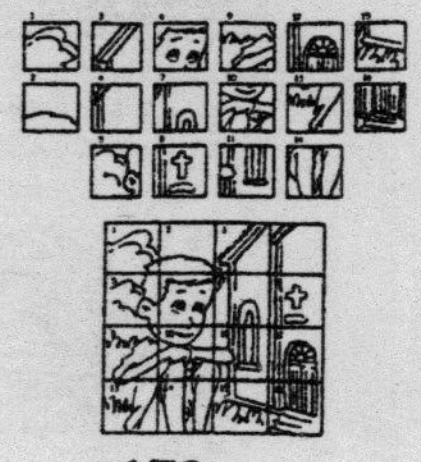

158

CONNECT THE DOTS

THERE IS NO CONDEMNATION FOR
THOSE WHO ARE IN JESUS CHRIST!

159

FINISH THE VERSE
TO FIND OUT WHAT THE VERSE BELOW SAYS, FILL
IN THE BLANKS. ALL THE CONSONANTS ARE THERE
SO ALL YOU NEED TO DO IS ADD THE VOWELS

VOWELS A E I O U

BUT YOU WERE WASHED,
YOU WERE SANCTIFIED
YOU WERE JUSTIFIED
IN.

BEFORE YOU
EVEN ASK...
"JUSTIFIED"
MEANS TO
BE MADE
FREE FROM
GUILT OR
BLAME

I KNEW
THAT!

160

CONT'D FROM THE PREVIOUS PAGE

THE NAME OF THE
LORD JESUS CHRIST
AND BY THE SPIRIT OF
OUR GOD.

1 CORINTHIANS 6:11

...AND "SANCTIFIED"
MEANS TO BE
MADE HOLY!

KNEW THAT
TOO

AH-HUH

I AM JUSTIFIED!

161

WORD SEARCH
CROSS OUT EVERY LETTER THAT APPEARS FOUR
TIMES IN THE PUZZLE TO FIND THE WORD THAT
COMPLETES THE SENTENCE

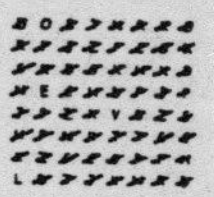

BECAUSE OF HIS GREAT L O V E FOR US
JESUS PAID THE PRICE FOR ALL OUR SINS!

162

LOOK-ALIKES
FIND AND CIRCLE TEN DIFFERENCES IN THE TWO
PICTURES BELOW

163

CODE BUSTER
USE THE CODE CHART BELOW TO COMPLETE THE
VERSE. CHOOSE FROM THE LEFT SET OF NUMBERS
FIRST (Eg. 23=J)

	1	2	3	4	5	6
1	A	B	C	D	E	F
2	G	H	I	J	K	L
3	M	N	O	P	Q	R
4	S	T	U	V	W	X

GOD MADE HIM WHO
HAD NO SIN TO BE
SIN FOR US SO
THAT IN HIM

CONT'D ON THE NEXT PAGE

164

CONT'D FROM THE PREVIOUS PAGE

WE MIGHT BECOME
THE RIGHTEOUS-
NESS OF GOD.

2 CORINTHIANS 5:21

JUST SO YOU KNOW...
"RIGHTEOUSNESS" ALSO
MEANS TO BE "FREE OF
GUILT". TO BE SEEN
AS RIGHTEOUS IN
GOD'S EYES

AHHH-
HAAHAA
HAAHAA

I HAVE HIS RIGHTEOUSNESS!

165

FILL IN THE BLANKS

"WE ARE THEREFORE CHRIST'S
AMBASSADORS AS
THOUGH GOD WERE MAKING HIS
APPEAL THROUGH US."

2 CORINTHIANS 5:20

I AM GOD'S REPRESENTATIVE!

166

TWICE THE FUN

UNSCRAMBLE THE UNDERLINED WORDS IN THE VERSE BELOW. THEN ON THE NEXT PAGE FIND AND CIRCLE THEM IN THE WORD SEARCH PUZZLE.

"IF WE _CONFESS_ OUR _SINS_, HE IS _FAITHFUL_ AND _JUST_ AND WILL _FORGIVE_ US OUR SINS AND _PURIFY_ US FROM ALL UNRIGHTEOUSNESS."

CONFESS SINS
FAITHFUL JUST
FORGIVE PURIFY

1 JOHN 1:9

168

CONT'D FROM THE PREVIOUS PAGE

I HAVE TO
ADMIT, THIS WAY
IS BETTER!

I AM COMPLETELY FORGIVEN!

169

ZANY CODE BUSTER

USE THE CODE CHART BELOW TO DECODE THE MYSTERY VERSE.

AND MY GOD
WILL MEET
ALL YOUR
NEEDS

CONT'D ON THE NEXT PAGE.

170

CONT'D FROM THE PREVIOUS PAGE

ACCORDING
TO HIS
GLORIOUS
RICHES IN
CHRIST
JESUS.

PHILIPPIANS 4:19

HE... HAD... NOT!
NEEDS, MY GUD...
NOT WANTS!

I HAVE MY NEEDS MET BY GOD!

171

ZANY CODE BUSTER

TO DECODE THIS MYSTERY VERSE, LOOK AT EACH LETTER AND WRITE THE ONE THAT COMES BEFORE IT IN THE ALPHABET.

ABCDEFGHIJKLMNOPQR
STUVWXYZ

I HAVE LOVED YOU
J IB WF MPWFE ZPV

WITH AN EVERLAST-
XJUI BO FWFSMBTU

ING LOVE.
JOH MPWF

JEREMIAH 31:3

I AM TENDERLY LOVED!

174

UNSCRAMBLE THE VERSE

TO FIND OUT WHAT THE VERSE BELOW SAYS, FILL IN THE BLANKS. ALL THE VOWELS ARE THERE SO ALL YOU NEED TO ADD ARE THE CONSONANTS.

"OER EW RSA OT OGD HET DARRA FO STHRRC RAMNG HETSO HWO EA RNESE VAESE HNO TERMD REA RIERSHNG."

"FOR WE ARE TO GOD
THE AROMA OF CHRIST
AMONG THOSE WHO ARE
BEING SAVED AND
THOSE WHO ARE PERISH-
ING."

2 CORINTHIANS 2:15

I AM A SWEET SMELL OF CHRIST TO
GOD!

175

FINISH THE VERSE

TO FIND OUT WHAT THE VERSE BELOW SAYS, FILL IN THE BLANKS. ALL THE CONSONANTS ARE THERE SO ALL YOU NEED TO DO IS ADD THE VOWELS.

VOWELS A E I O U

"FOR WE ARE THE
TEMPLE OF THE LIVING
GOD."

2 CORINTHIANS 6:16

YOU KNOW, WARREN...
WE REALLY NEED
TO TALK...

I AM THE TEMPLE OF GOD!

176

CODE BUSTER

USE THE CODE CHART BELOW TO COMPLETE THE VERSE. CHOOSE FROM THE LEFT SET OF NUMBERS FIRST (Ex: E3=J)

	1	2	3	4	5	6	7
1	A	B	C	D	E	F	G
2	H	I	J	K	L	M	N
3	O	P	Q	R	S	T	U
4	V	W	X	Y	Z		

BUT NOW HE HAS
RECONCILED YOU
BY CHRIST'S PHY-
SICAL BODY

CONT'D ON THE NEXT PAGE

177

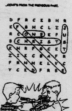

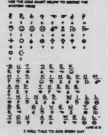

CONT'D FROM THE PREVIOUS PAGE

THROUGH DEATH

TO PRESENT YOU

HOLY IN HIS SIGHT,

WITHOUT BLEMISH

AND FREE FROM

ACCUSATION.

COLOSSIANS 1:22

I AM BLAMELESS AND BEYOND REPROACH!

178

ZANY CODE BUSTER

USE THE CODE CHART BELOW TO DECODE THE MYSTERY VERSE

BUT SEEK FIRST HIS KINGDOM AND HIS RIGHTEOUSNESS AND ALL THESE THINGS WILL BE GIVEN TO YOU AS WELL.

LUKE 12:31

I WILL TALK TO GOD EVERY DAY

180

UNSCRAMBLE THE VERSE

TO FIND OUT WHAT THE VERSE BELOW SAYS FILL IN THE BLANKS. ALL THE VOWELS ARE THERE SO ALL YOU NEED TO ADD ARE THE CONSONANTS

COMMIT YOUR WAYS TO THE LORD TRUST IN HIM AND HE WILL MAKE YOUR RIGHTEOUSNESS SHINE LIKE THE DAWN.

PSALMS 37:5,6

I WILL COMMIT MY WAYS TO THE LORD

181

FINISH THE VERSE

TO FIND OUT WHAT THE VERSE BELOW SAYS FILL IN THE BLANKS. ALL THE CONSONANTS ARE THERE SO ALL YOU NEED TO DO IS ADD THE VOWELS

VOWELS: A E I O U

"THIS IS THE DAY THE LORD HAS MADE. LET US REJOICE AND BE GLAD IN IT."

PSALMS 118:24

I WILL MAKE TODAY MY BEST DAY

184

CODE BUSTER

USE THE CODE CHART BELOW TO COMPLETE THE VERSE. CHOOSE FROM THE LEFT SET OF NUMBERS FIRST (top to bottom)

	1	2	3	4	5	6	7
1	A	B	C	D	E	F	G
2	H	I	J	K	L	M	N
3	O	P	Q	R	S	T	U
4	V	W	X	Y	Z		

WHATEVER HAPPENS. CONDUCT YOURSELVES IN A MANNER WORTHY OF THE GOSPEL OF CHRIST.

PHILIPPIANS 1:27

185

TWICE THE FUN

UNSCRAMBLE THE UNDERLINED WORDS IN THE VERSE BELOW. THEN ON THE NEXT PAGE FIND AND CIRCLE THEM IN THE WORD SEARCH PUZZLE

"BE KIND AND COMPASSIONATE TO ONE ANOTHER FORGIVING EACH OTHER. JUST AS IN CHRIST GOD FORGAVE YOU."

KIND ONE JUST CHRIST FORGAVE

EPHESIANS 4:32

CONT'D ON THE NEXT PAGE

186

CONT'D FROM THE PREVIOUS PAGE.

I WILL BE KIND TO OTHERS

187

PICTURE FRAMES

WHAT COULD THE PICTURE BE?

DRAW EXACTLY WHAT IS IN EACH NUMBERED FRAME AT THE TOP OF THE PAGE INTO EACH FRAME OF THE SAME NUMBER IN THE GRID BELOW

188

ZANY CODE BUSTER

TO DECODE THIS MYSTERY VERSE, LOOK AT EACH LETTER AND WRITE THE ONE THAT COMES BEFORE IT IN THE ALPHABET

A B C D E F G H I J K L M N O P Q R S T U V W X Y Z

"I CAN DO EVERY- THING THROUGH HIM WHO GIVES ME STRENGTH"

PHILIPPIANS 4:13

I WILL DO WHAT I'M ASKED WITHOUT COMPLAINT

189

UNSCRAMBLE THE VERSE

TO FIND OUT WHAT THE VERSE BELOW SAYS, FILL IN THE BLANKS. ALL THE VOWELS ARE THERE SO ALL YOU NEED TO ADD ARE THE CONSONANTS.

"BE VERY CAREFUL, THEN, HOW YOU LIVE - NOT AS UNWISE BUT AS WISE, MAKING THE MOST OF EVERY OPPORTUNITY BECAUSE THE DAYS ARE EVIL."

—EPHESIANS 5:15,16

I WILL MAKE THE MOST OF EVERY OPPORTUNITY

190

MULTIPLE CHOICE

CIRCLE THE CORRECT ANSWER

1. WE SHOULD PUT OUR TRUST IN
   A. MONEY
   B. THE LORD
   C. FRIENDS

2. WHAT MUST WE SEEK TO BE GIVEN ALL THINGS?
   A. A JOB
   B. A RAISE IN OUR ALLOWANCE
   C. GOD'S KINGDOM

3. EVERYONE WHO HAS WILL BE GIVEN
   MATTHEW 25:29

I WILL USE MY TALENTS EVERY DAY

191

ZANY CODE BUSTER

USE THE CODE CHART BELOW TO DECODE THE MYSTERY VERSE

AND WE KNOW THAT IN ALL THINGS GOD WORKS FOR

CONT'D ON THE NEXT PAGE

192

CONT'D FROM THE PREVIOUS PAGE.

THE GOOD OF THOSE WHO LOVE HIM, WHO HAVE BEEN CALLED ACCORDING TO HIS PURPOSE.

—ROMANS 8:28

I WILL TRUST GOD TO WORK EVERYTHING OUT

193

FILL IN THE BLANKS

VOCABULARY	
HELPFUL	BENEFIT
NEEDS	UNWHOLESOME
ACCORDING	LISTEN
TALK	MOUTHS

"DO NOT LET ANY UNWHOLESOME TALK COME OUT OF YOUR MOUTHS, BUT ONLY WHAT IS HELPFUL FOR BUILDING OTHERS UP"

CONT'D ON THE NEXT PAGE

194

CONT'D FROM THE PREVIOUS PAGE.

ACCORDING TO THEIR NEEDS THAT IT MAY BENEFIT THOSE WHO LISTEN.

—EPHESIANS 4:29

I WILL ENCOURAGE OTHERS TO BE ALL GOD CREATED THEM TO BE

195

CODE BUSTER

USE THE CODE CHART BELOW TO COMPLETE THE VERSE. CHOOSE FROM THE LEFT SET OF NUMBERS FIRST (eg. 3>J)

	1	2	3	4	5	6	7
1	A	B	C	D	E	F	G
2	H	I	J	K	L	M	N
3	O	P	Q	R	S	T	U
4	V	W	X	Y	Z		

DO NOT BE ANXIOUS ABOUT ANYTHING, BUT IN EVERYTHING, BY PRAYER

CONT'D ON THE NEXT PAGE

196

CONT'D FROM THE PREVIOUS PAGE.

AND PETITION, WITH THANKSGIVING, PRESENT YOUR REQUESTS TO GOD.

—PHILIPPIANS 4:6

I WILL NOT PANIC...I WILL PRAY

197

SEE YA' NEXT TIME!